365 Folk Tales

Om Books International

Reprinted in 2019

Corporate & Editorial Office
A-12, Sector 64, Noida 201 301
Uttar Pradesh, India
Phone: +91 120 477 4100
Email: editorial@ombooks.com
Website: www.ombooksinternational.com

Sales Office
107, Ansari Road, Darya Ganj
New Delhi 110 002, India
Phone: +91 11 4000 9000
Email: sales@ombooks.com
Website: www.ombooks.com

ISBN: 978-81-87107-56-9

Printed in India

10 9 8 7

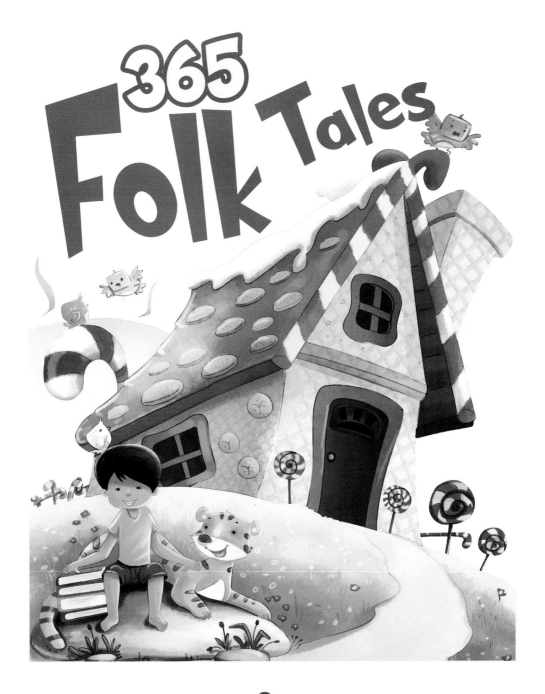

365 Folk Tales

An imprint of Om Books International

Contents

The Story of the Month: Where Stories Came From

The Story of the Month

Where Stories Came From

01 Where Stories Came From

A long, long time ago, in the wild forests of Africa, there lived a woodcutter called Zenzele and his wife Manzandaba. Zenzele went to the forests every morning, while his wife looked after their three children and finished all the household chores.

The children collected beautiful flowers from the garden, chased the crabs into the sea and rejoiced when they saw a rainbow in the sky. When they would get bored, they asked their mother to tell them a story. But Manzandaba had no stories to tell, for she didn't know what stories were. So she asked her husband if he knew any stories. "Stories? I am a wood cutter. How would I know any stories?" replied Zenzele. "Why don't you ask the grand old tortoise in the forest if he knows any!" he suggested.

Manzandaba rushed to meet the grand old tortoise, who lived inside a cave. "Oh Manzandaba! I am very old now and cannot recall any tales. Why don't you go to Hooty Owl, for she stays awake all night and roams the entire forest!" said the grand old tortoise.

As soon as dusk fell, Manzandaba went to meet Hooty Owl. "Hooty Owl, please tell me some stories for my children are getting bored and I don't know any!" urged Manzandaba. "Hoot-hoot-hoot! Go away, this is no time to tell stories, its time for me to have dinner now!" shouted an angry Hooty.

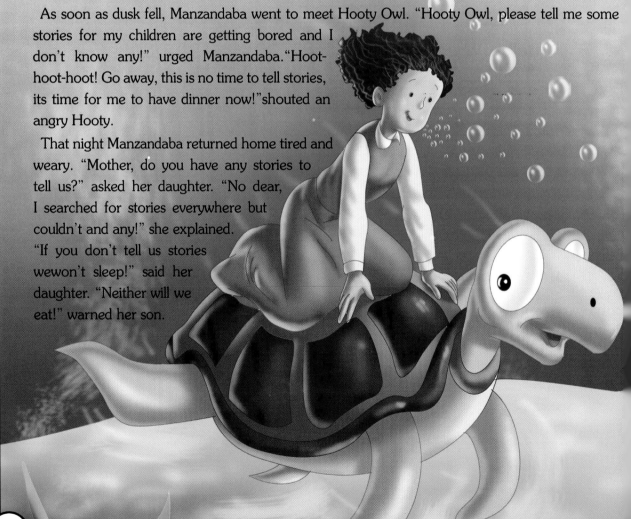

That night Manzandaba returned home tired and weary. "Mother, do you have any stories to tell us?" asked her daughter. "No dear, I searched for stories everywhere but couldn't and any!" she explained. "If you don't tell us stories wewon't sleep!" said her daughter. "Neither will we eat!" warned her son.

Manzandaba was very worried now. She sat on the seashore and cried, "God, please help me and some stories!" Suddenly, she heard someone say, "Why is beautiful Manzandaba shedding her precious tears?" It was the sea turtle. "My children won't eat or sleep if I don't tell them stories!" cried Manzandaba. "Well, children need stories, for that's how they learn about pretty fairies and princesses and brave kings and wicked giants," explained the wise turtle. "Then tell me some such tales!" said Manzandaba, her eyes lighting up. "I can take you to the place where stories come from!" replied the turtle. The turtle asked Manzandaba to climb on its back and then he swam towards the seabed. Amidst the shes and colourful plants, there was a mermaid. She had long golden tresses, sparkling eyes and a lovely blue tail. "Welcome to my land!" she said with a warm smile. "Can you tell me some stories?" asked an anxious Manzandaba. "Sure! But what will you give me in return?" asked the mermaid. "Whatever you want." promised Manzandaba.
"Then bring me a picture of your home and your people!" replied the mermaid. "But what will you do with pictures of my family?" asked Manzandaba. "I am a mermaid and I can never go to the dry lands. If you give me a picture of your people then I can weave a story by seeing it!" explained the mermaid.

Manzandaba quickly returned with a picture and the mermaid told her some fascinating tales. This way Manzandaba learnt some new stories and narrated them to her children every day.

02 How the Camel Got Its Hump

A long time ago, when God made the world, the camel did not have a hump. He used to be a very lazy camel. All day long, he chewed sticks and thorns and milkweed and prickles. The other animals wondered how to make the camel more like them. One day, the horse said, "Oh Camel, what a wonderful day! Why don't you come out for a trot with me?" The camel just said, "Humph!" and walked away. Later,the ox went to the camel and asked him to help him carry his load. "Humph!" said the camel. When the dog asked the camel to share his duty of guarding their kingdom, he just turned his face way. The angry animals decided to teach the camel a lesson. They went to the jinn of the desert and asked him to help them. The next day, the ox asked the camel,"What is that on your back?" When the camel looked, he realised to his shock that his back had grown into a hump. "Oh, my back! My back!" he wailed. "That's your punishment for being lazy," said the jinn. Ever since, the camel has a hump.

03 The Legend of the First Rainbow

A farmer had a beautiful garden full of golden flowers. One day, he built a wall around his garden but when he woke up in the morning, he was puzzled to see that the wall had crumbled down. He built the wall again but alas! Next morning, the wall was in shambles again. This continued for many days. Tired of building the wall over and over again, one day, the farmer decided to stay awake and catch the culprit. That night, he saw three fairies come from heaven and knock down his wall. Two of the fairies flew away when they saw the farmer but the third couldn't escape because the farmer hid her magic wings. After a few days, the farmer married the fairy and soon they had a son. The farmer loved the fairy and was very happy. One day, when the farmer was away, the fairy found her magic wings in a small, dark cupboard in the house. She was overjoyed. She wore them and went back to heaven with her little son. The farmer was very sad and wept for his wife and son. The gods took pity on the farmer's condition and made a rainbow so that he could climb up the sky to meet his family whenever he wanted.

04 The Shepherd's Mistake

A shepherd took out his sheep to graze every morning. He would sit and watch while the sheep fed on the fresh grass. One day, while the sheep were grazing, the shepherd saw a wolf eyeing his sheep from a distance. At first, the shepherd was afraid lest the wolf would harm his folck. But the wolf did not try to attack the sheep. Instead, he quietly followed the sheep home. Gradually, the shepherd's fear of the wolf subsided. One day, the shepherd was urgently called home. Thinking that his sheep would be safe with the wolf, he left them in the wolf's care. But when he returned, he was dismayed to and that the wolf had eaten up most of the sheep. Sitting down with his hands on his head, the shepherd moaned, "It was my fault. I was foolish to trust a wolf to guard my sheep."

05 The Golden Fish

An old fisherman and his wife lived in a small hut by the seaside. They were very poor and hardly had enough to eat. One day the fisherman caught a little golden fish. "Spare me and I'll do whatever you want," said the fish in a human voice. The fisherman took pity and let it go. When here turned home empty handed, his wife was very angry and shouted, "Just go and get some food from the fish." The fisherman did as he was told. The fish gave him food every day. Soon, the fisherman became very rich. Days passed and his wife became greedier. Not satisfied with their wealth, she wanted to become a queen. The magical fish granted this wish too. But the fisherman's wife ill-treated him. At last when she desired to become the ruler of the seas, the sea water became black and the golden fish disappeared forever and along with it the palace, the guards and all servants vanished. Once again the old man and his wife became poor.

06 The Sunflower

Clytie was a beautiful sea nymph. She had gorgeous yellow curls and a fine pink complexion. All the sea animals loved Clytie for she was warm and friendly.

One sunny morning when Clytie woke up, she heard her friend, Serena the mermaid sing a melodious song about a golden light. "A golden light?" asked Clytie. "Yes, it's the most radiant light and it spreads its warmth across the whole universe," replied Serena. "I want to see the light!" said Clytie. Serena and Clytie swam to the surface. "Look, it's there high up in the sky!" said a thrilled Serena as she pointed to the big golden sun. Clytie stood gazing at the dazzling sun and refused to go back home. As days passed, her long golden tresses slowly changed to bright yellow petals and her dainty feet into nimble roots. Clytie had become a sunflower! To this day the sunflower gazes at the sun high up in the sky and receives its golden warmth.

07 Cats and Rats

A long time ago, there lived a king who had a very faithful cat for a housekeeper and a rat for a houseboy. Now the rat fell in love with one of the servant girls. But being very poor, he could not give her any presents.

He thought of an idea. Every night, he entered the king's store through a small hole in the roof. He took corn and pears from there and gave them to his sweetheart.

At the end of the month, the cat had to give an account of the things in the store. When the king saw so much corn and pears missing, he demanded an explanation from the cat.

The cat was unable to explain. That evening her friend told her what the rat had been doing.

When the king was informed about this, he ordered for the servant girl to be put behind bars. As for the rat, he was given to the cat and you can guess what the cat did. Since then, cats and rats are enemies.

08 The Legend of the Dipper

Once upon a time, a poor little girl lived with her mother in a small cottage in the woods. One day, her mother fell ill. Since there was no water in the house, the little girl had to go out to fetch some water for her mother.

As she was walking back home, she met a very thirsty dog. Though there was very little water in the dipper, she poured some into the dog's mouth. And lo! The wooden dipper was transformed into silver and was full again. Too tired to notice the change, the girl met a thirsty stranger a little further down the road. She held the dipper to the man's lips and this time, the dipper was changed into gold. Finally the girl reached home. After drinking the water, her mother quickly regained her health and became strong again. This time the dipper was filled up with diamonds and sparkling jewels. The girl's mother was delighted. Now all their problems were solved and they were no longer poor.

09 The Last Wish

The brahmins in the court of King Krishnadevrai were very greedy. One day the king said to them, "My dying mother's last wish was to eat a mango. But no mangoes were available then. Is there any way I can make her soul rest in peace?" "Your Majesty, you should donate 108 mangoes made of pure gold to brahmins," said one brahmin. Tenalirama, the witty and intelligent minister of the king, decided to teach the greedy brahmins a lesson. At the funeral feast held in honour of the King's mother, Tenalirama ordered the servants to touch the brahmins' feet with red-hot iron rods. The king was puzzled so Tenalirama explained, "Your Highness, my dead mother was suffering from arthritis. Before dying she wished that her feet be touched with red-hot iron. But I could not fulfill her wish. If your mother's soul can rest in peace by giving golden mangoes to these brahmins, then surely my dead mother's soul too can be comforted by touching the brahmins' feet with hot iron rods." The king had a hearty laugh at Tenalirama's clever logic while the brahmins bowed their heads in shame.

10 Tortoise, the Birds and the Feast

There was a famine in the forest and Tortoise was starving. He heard about the feast given by the sky god to the birds. "I should somehow attend the feast" thought Tortoise and convinced the birds to take him with them. They stuck feathers to his arms and he could fly. "Call me, All of You, in my new appearance," said Tortoise on the way. The birds agreed. The sky god welcomed them and said pointing at the delicious food platters, "This is for all for you,". Tortoise at once told the birds that the food was meant only for him and ate up everything while the birds watched. Feeling cheated, the birds decided to teach the sly Tortoise a lesson. So they invited Tortoise to another feast held for them on the land. When Tortoise reached the place, a bird announced that no one could eat with dirty claws. Tortoise rushed to the pond to clean himself but every time he dirtied his limbs while walking back. "Watch as we eat," mocked the birds and laughed at Tortoise's plight.

11 The Honeybee's Sting

Zeus is the protector of this universe. In Greek mythology he is the deity of thunder and lightning. One day, the honeybee came to Zeus and said, "My Lord, please grant me my wish!" "Of course, little creature. Speak! What is your wish?" asked Zeus. "My Lord, please give me the power of inflicting great pain on others." "Oh, what a cruel desire!" exclaimed Zeus angrily. "Yes, but you have given me your word. I hope you will not deny me my wish!" said the honeybee.

"I shall fulfill what you desire on one condition," said Zeus firmly. "And what is that, my Lord?" asked the little creature. "You must use sound judgement before causing any harm to others and you shall be able to use your sting only once in your lifetime!" Even today the honeybee gets to use its sting only once, after which it dies.

12 Legend of Little Statesmanly

Long ago, in the country of Vietnam, there lived a man named Statesmanly. He was very small—as small as a thumb. However, Statesmanly was very intelligent and the king offered him the post of a minister in his kingdom. One day, a dispute surfaced between China and Vietnam and the king sent Statesmanly to resolve the matter. When Statesmanly arrived in China, the people were shocked to see him.

"Oh, look at him, he looks like a dwarf!" they joked. Turning a deaf ear to their comments, Statesmanly walked in proudly to meet the Chinese Emperor. The emperor looked down from his dragon throne at Statesmanly and remarked, "How can a tiny man like you solve such a big problem?" Statesmanly stepped forward and replied, "Oh, don't worry Sir, in our country we send big men to solve big matters and short ones for smaller problems. I will solve this matter in no time!" The Chinese Emperor was very impressed with Statesmanly's ready wit and helped him to resolve the problem amicably.

13 The Wise Ant and the Lazy Grasshopper

Autumn was coming to an end. The sun had mellowed, the leaves had turned orange and a chilly breeze swayed throughout the day. The lazy grasshopper loved autumn for this was the season when he could spend his days playing. He hopped from leaf to leaf and from one fallen twig to another.

While the grasshopper was playing, an ant trudged along with a rice grain. "Why don't you play with me instead of pulling that huge piece of grain!" asked the jubilant grasshopper. "Oh! Don't you know how hard it is to gather food during winter!" replied the tiny ant and went home.

"What a foolish creature she is!" thought the lazy grasshopper. "I'd much rather enjoy than bother myself about the winters." Then winter came. The trees had no leaves or fruits and the rice fields were covered with thick snow. The grasshopper searched day and night for some food but could not find any. He grew very weak and then cried, 'How I wasted my days playing when I should have worked hard to gather food!"

14 The Kaha Bird

The people of Afghanistan have for very long believed that a magical bird named Kaha comes down from heaven to help the poor and the needy. Long ago, there lived a poor fisherman. One day, he prayed to God to help him in his distress. Suddenly, the magical bird Kaha came swooping down and said, "Do not worry. I shall pick the finest fish from the river and you can sell them in the market." As promised, Kaha brought the biggest and often the most delicious fish from the river for the fisherman. The fisherman became famous for his delicious fish and was soon a rich man. However, he was soon filled with greed and thought, "If I cage that bird, it will grant all my wishes and then I will be the richest man in the country!" That night the fisherman crept stealthily behind the bird and caught it. He was about to put Kaha inside a cage, when it spread its huge wings and soared up to the sky. The startled fisherman realised that Kaha was a magical bird. He repented his greed but it was too late.

15 Ship of the Desert

Long ago, there was no system of transport in the deserts and travellers who crossed these vast stretches of sand had to face many difficulties.

One day while walking across the desert, a man suddenly saw a camel. "What a weird creature it is!" thought the man, "It is tall, has a funny hump on its back and is very meek!" After a while the camel quietly walked up to a small pool of water and drank some water. Suddenly, the man heard some loud grunts coming from a distance. He turned his head and found many such animals coming his way. "They must be very strong, they can walk the entire length of the desert and survive only on some water and dry desert plants!" thought the man. "Maybe should tame him and make him my vehicle." The man concluded. Since then, the camel transports man and goods and is called 'the ship of the desert'.

16 The Legend Of the Christmas Spider

Long ago in Germany, a mother was cleaning her house just before Christmas. "I don't want a speck of dust here!" said the finicky lady. "Those horrible cobwebs, they should disappear right away!" she thought as she beat every nook and corner with a rag. The poor little spiders jumped on the floor and rushed towards a hole in the wall.

In the evening when the children of the house decorated the Christmas tree, a baby spider said, "Why is that huge tree being decorated?" "It's Christmas time dear, when Lord Jesus visits people's homes," explained the mother. "I want to see Jesus," said the baby spider. At night the spiders   came out of hiding and climbed the Christmas tree. Lord Jesus, who was watching from the heavens above, blessed the little creatures. Within seconds, they turned into shimmering gold and silver spiders and made the tree look even more beautiful. Since then it has become a custom to include a spider among the decorations on the Christmas tree.

17 Marriage of the Mouse

Mr. Mouse was searching for a bride. However, finding a worthy wife was becoming difficult since he was extremely proud of his looks. At last his parents sought the help of the gods. "Could you give us a wife for our son?" they asked. "Oh, there's no one among us who can match your son's qualities, you should look for a bride in the wind family," suggested the gods. When the mouse family went to the winds, they said, "It's true, that we are powerful and can raise a storm, but we are nothing as compared to the mighty mountains. Your son should marry someone from among the tall mountains." The mouse family now approached the mountain, which heard their problem patiently and replied, "I am strong but then there's one tiny creature that still manages to make gaping holes in my sides!" "Who is that mighty creature?" asked the mouse family curiously. "It's a mouse!' replied the mountain and continued, "You must choose her as your bride!"

The handsome mouse finally married another mouse and both lived happily ever after.

11

18 The King's White Elephant

Long ago, a king had a beautiful white elephant. One day, while roaming in the forest, the elephant injured his leg. A group of woodcutters saw the elephant groaning in pain and rushed to help. They cleaned his wound and looked after him. Thankful for curing his wound, the elephant decided to stay back and help the men. The elephant began collecting the wood and carried it on its back. After a few years the woodcutters' trade flourished and they became rich men. However, now the elephant grew old and could no longer carry heavy logs. The woodcutters refused to look after it and left the animal. Meanwhile, the king came to the forest one day. He suddenly discovered his white elephant lying in a quiet corner, weary and tired. The king understood what had happened and punished the woodcutters for being so cruel to the animal. The white elephant recognised his master and went back to the king's castle.

19 The Mulla Pleads Poverty

Mulla Nasruddin once borrowed a large sum of money from a money lender and failed to return it on time. The money lender went to the court and Mulla was brought before the judge. On being asked by the judge, Mulla admitted to have borrowed hundred dinars and promised to return it even if he had to sell his cow or his horse. Hearing him, the moneylender shouted out, "My Lord, He's lying. He doesn't have a horse or a cow. In fact, he doesn't even have food in the house to feed his wife and children." At this the Mulla smiled and said very wittily, "My Lord, if he knows that I'm so poor, doesn't he know that I am not in a position to return this money immediately." The judge heard the Mulla and dismissed the case.

20 The Costliest Gift

King Krishnadevaraya, in whose court Tenalirama served as the official jester, had won a crucial battle. To celebrate his victory, the king was distributing some valuable gifts among his subjects. When these gifts were being distributed, Tenalirama was ill and had to stay at home. The day he came to court, he was given a silver bowl. The other court jesters who were jealous of Tenalirama's position in the court were very happy to see him get the paltry gift. "An empty silver bowl is what the King's favourite jester has got!" they joked. Tenalirama hid the bowl with a scarf and was about to leave when the king said, "Why are you hiding that silver bowl. Aren't you happy with this gift?" The wise courtier now turned to his king and said, "My Lord, I am only trying to hide the bowl because people might believe that King Krishnadevaraya is capable of giving only such paltry gifts to his people!" The king felt very ashamed and immediately gave Tenalirama an expensive diamond ring. Tenalirama smiled and walked away with the costliest gift.

21 The Leprechaun's Gold

One sunny day, a farmer called Christopher saw a tiny man in a red hat sitting near a hedge. "Well, that looks like a leprechaun," said a delighted Christopher. "I've heard that they hide a pot of gold nearby. If I'm able to find it, then I won't have to worry for the rest of my life." Christopher quickly grabbed the leprechaun and demanded, "Where have you hidden the gold?" "First, take me to that field below that mountain," said the frightened little man. The leprechaun pointed to the corner of the field and said, "The gold is under that tree." Since Christopher did not have anything to dig the earth with, he tied a small red cloth on one of the branches. "This will help me remember where to dig for the gold. Promise me that you will not untie that cloth," said Christopher and dropped the leprechaun. Christopher soon returned with a shovel. But to his utter bewilderment, all the trees in the field had red cloths tied on their branches and the leprechaun too had vanished. Poor Christopher walked home without any gold.

22 Rivers and the Sea

Many years ago, the rivers were unhappy and dissatisfied. They started off as tiny streams in the mountains, flowed through ravines, plains and plateaus and ultimately merged with the big seas. They held an urgent meeting. "This is not fair," said one of the river. "Why do we have to join the sea and lose our freedom? Our sweet and clean water becomes dirty and salty when we enter the sea." "That's right. When we can survive floods and droughts, then I think we are capable of surviving on our own forever," said another annoyed river. The sea was amused by the rivers' discussion. "If that's how you feel, then do not join me. Go and live on your own," said the sea. Then one wise river spoke, "If we don't join the sea, we will dry up during the dry season and ultimately we will all die." The other rivers realised the truth behind his words. So they decided it was better to join the sea and flow together in harmony.

23 Why the Sky is So High

A long time ago, the sky was very close to the earth. In those days, a bent old woman lived in a small thatched hut. The hut stood high on the mountain, where the sky was especially low. The bent old woman had an odd habit. She was always cleaning, scrubbing and dusting every corner of her little hut. One summer, the land became very dry and dusty. There was dust everywhere—on the trees, the leaves, the roofs, in the air and even in people's eyes and throats. The old woman swept and swept her hut with her broom but the more she swept, the more dust gathered.

The poor sky began to choke with all the dust that the old woman raised with her broom. It sneezed loudly and its eyes began to water. Finally, the sky was fed up with the dusty earth. It decided to move higher up where the air was clean. So the sky flew higher and higher and still remains high up even to this day.

24 The Enormous Nose

Many years ago, an enchantress cursed a king for laughing at her long nose. "You will have a son whose nose will be very long till the day he realises it," she said. The queen soon gave birth to a baby boy whose nose was indeed very long. Seeing the king and the queen upset, the king's minister said, "Your Majesty, all great people have a long nose. The prince's nose is not so long after all."

The prince was never made to realise by anyone about his unusually long nose. When he was old enough to get married, he went to meet the beautiful Princess Rosemarie. When he bent down to kiss her hand, he could not raise her hand to his lips for his long nose came in the way. "It seems I have a very long nose," said the shocked prince. Suddenly, the enchantress appeared and laughed, "At last you know what it is like to have a long nose." The next moment, to the complete amazement of all, the prince's nose returned to normal size.

25 How a Coyote Stole Fire

Long ago, Summer and Autumn were the only seasons on Earth. A coyote enjoyed this warm, pleasant weather. One day, the coyote was surprised to notice that the weather had suddenly become cold. Man was very worried. He had no protective fur like animals so he felt very cold. The coyote decided to help man.

"I must go to the three Fire Beings who live in the mountains," the coyote thought.

The Fire Beings had once got hold of a piece of the sun and guarded it fiercely. The coyote set off for the mountains until he reached the camp of the Fire Beings. He watched the fire beings and waited for them to go to sleep. Then he leapt at the glowing piece of fire and picked it up and ran down the mountain. Hearing the noise, the Fire Beings woke up and chased the coyote. They had almost caught him when the coyote threw away the piece of fire towards Man. The coyote later realised that his tail had turned white. So that's the secret of the coyote's white-tipped tail.

26 Origin of the Tiger

Once upon a time, there lived a great king. In those days it was a common practice to use magical powers in order to win wars. As the king grew older, he used to worry that enemies would overtake his kingdom since he did not possess any magical powers. As days passed, the king became sad and upset. The queen worried about the king's health and often tried to console him but to no avail.

One day, the royal astrologer came to meet the king. He suggested that the king, queen and the four chief ministers along with him should learn magic from Tisabamokkha who lived in Taxila, in the northwestern part of India. The king happily agreed and they went to meet Tisabamokkha.

On their journey back to the kingdom after spending a week with Tisabamokkha, the group lost their way in the forest. All the food they had brought with them was soon finished. "Let's use the magic we learnt. We shall transform ourselves into a ferocious animal. That way we will be able to hunt other animals for food," said the astrologer.

So the king was transformed into the head of the animal, the queen into the body, the astrologer became the tail and the chief ministers were turned into the four legs of the animal.

That is how the first tiger came upon the Earth.

27 The Little Match Girl

It was a cold December day. A little match girl walked barefoot on the wet, snow-covered road, holding her bundle of matchsticks close to her chest. She looked very pale and weak. "Oh! I couldn't sell even one matchstick today. I'm sure father will be angry," cried the poor match girl. Shivering in the cold, she took shelter in the corner of a big verandah of a multistoried building. Trying her best to cover herself with the scarf she had, the little girl tried to forget her hunger by closing her eyes. "I wish I could make merry and celebrate Christmas this year," thought the match girl as she dozed off to sleep. "Hey! Little One, Cheer up. You'll indeed have a terrific Christmas this year. I'll turn all your matchsticks into gold. Go home and give them to your father. He'll be very happy," she heard Santa say in her dream. She woke up with a jerk and looked around. There was no sign of Santa. Suddenly her eyes fell on the pile of matchsticks and she jumped up saying, "My dream has come true…" She picked up the golden matchsticks and ran home happily.

28 The Clever Brahmin

A king had a black dog whom he loved dearly. Once, while the king was away hunting, his dog got lost in the forest. Bereaved, the king declared, "Whosoever can find my dog will be handsomely rewarded." A clever Brahmin heard about this. He got the details of the king's dog from the royal priest. Now it so happened that a dog of the same breed as the king's was owned by one of the Brahmin's neighbour. It looked exactly like the king's dog except that it was white in colour. "All I need to do is dye its fur black, and then I'm sure the king will easily believe that it is his dog," thought the sly Brahmin. One day when his neighbour was away, the Brahmin lured the dog into his hut and dipped it in a bucket full of black dye and lo! It looked exactly like the king's lost dog. Next morning, the Brahmin took the dog to the palace. The moment the king saw the dog, he mistook it be his lost dog and hugged it. He rewarded the Brahmin handsomely, who immediately left the kingdom and went to settle in a faraway land.

29 The Day the Sky Fell

One day, Chicken Little was having some worms in the farmyard when an acorn fell from the tree and hit Chicken Little's head. "Oh! The sky is falling. I need to go and tell the king," thought Chicken Little and started running towards the king's palace. On the way, his friends Henny Penny, Ducky Lucky, Goosey Loosey and Turkey Lurkey joined him. Seeing them running in a hurry, Foxy Loxy volunteered to take them to the palace through a shortcut. But alas! He took them to his den and as they were about to enter, Little Squirrel warned them about Foxy Loxy's intention of having them for supper and they all ran away in different directions to their homes.

30 The Legend of the Christmas Rose

On the birth of Christ, the three Magi's offered gifts of myrrh, frankincense and old to baby Christ rejoicing his birth. But a poor shepherd maiden stood on the threshold of the manger, weeping bitterly for she had nothing to offer the new born, not even a rose flower for it was all covered with snow. An angel saw her and brushed aside the snow on her feet. And lo! A bunch of beautiful white roses lay by her feet. The maiden was overjoyed. She picked up the roses and kissed the snow white petals thinking, "The beauty of these flowers outwits all precious gifts," and rushed to the manger to offer the white winter roses to the holy child.

31 The Masquerader

The royal priest in the kingdom of King Krishnadevaraya was very jealous of Tenalirama. He decided to get rid of him. On the pretext of going to a holy place, the priest left the capital. He spent this time to learn the art of disguise.

After some time, he returned to the kingdom in disguise. The disguised priest boasted of his abilities to all people. The king heard about the newcomer and demanded that he should be brought before him. "I hear you are a master of disguise," said the king. "Let me see what you can do!" "I can turn myself into a lion," said the priest. "I have heard so much about Tenalirama that I want him to be present when I give my show."

The king readily agreed.

During the show, the priest leapt at Tenalirama. Tenalirama had suspected that this person was an impostor and an enemy. So he had worn armour under his clothes. He took out his sword and attacked the impostor.

"Tell me, who are you?" demanded Tenalirama.

The priest cried in pain. His real identity was exposed before all. The enraged king banished him from his service.

Contents

The Story of the Month: Rere, the Disobedient Son

The Story of the Month

Rere, the Disobedient Son

01 Rere, the Disobedient Son

Oluwa was a rich man and a loving father. He had three sons. He loved his sons a lot and gave them whatever they wanted. But Rere, the youngest of the three, was not satisfied with the comforts of his house. One morning, he went to his father and said, "Father, I want to go to the forest and practice hunting." Oluwa was surprised to hear his twelve-year-old son. "You are too young to go to the forest all alone. The wild beasts will harm you," said Oluwa to discourage his adamant son. But Rere was determined. Unwilling to disappoint his son, Oluwa got a few animals and a gun and said, "Rere, why don't you practice hunting at home? I've made the necessary arrangements." But Rere was still not satisfied. Next morning, without informing anybody, Rere left for the forest with his big knife and gun. He went deep into the forest looking for an animal to hunt. Suddenly it started to rain heavily and Rere hid in a tree hole. Slowly it became dark but the rains continued pouring. Deciding to return home, Rere came out of his hideout and began walking in the rain. He lost his way and came to a big stream. As he swam across the stream, he was caught amidst a torrent and almost fainted. Fortunately, Tortoise, the jungle drummer, was nearby and saw Rere. "Gosh! He's drowning. I must save him," thought Tortoise and carried Rere ashore. He took Rere to his house and nursed him. Rere enjoyed a hearty meal with Tortoise and sang out his tale in a melodious note:

O' I'm Oluwa's disobedient son

Was out for hunting thinking it be fun

But here I lay

With a price of slavery to pay

"Hmmm… you're a disobedient young fellow," said Tortoise thoughtfully. Impressed by Rere's sweet voice, he contrived a plan to detain Rere with him and use his melodious voice for his benefit.

Tortoise made a huge drum and invited Rere to look at it from the inside. Assoon as Rere stepped in, Tortoise quickly sealed it with antelope's skin. He then took it to the king who had invited him for a performance in his court. As soon as Rere started singing with the drumbeat, everyone including the king, got up and started dancing merrily. The king was so pleased that he gave half of his kingdom to Tortoise.

Meanwhile, Rere's parents had been frantically looking for him and as per the Wise Man's advice, invited Tortoise for a feast and got him drunk. While the Tortoise lay fast asleep, Rere's father broke open the drum and freed Rere. "Oh Father, I'm so sorry to have disobeyed you," said Rere as they hugged each other. His mother too welcomed him with open arms.

The next morning, when Tortoise lifted his drum, he came to realise that Rere had escaped. He shouted in anger, "Who has fiddled with my drum?" Just then Oluwa came out with a big stick and hit Tortoise hard on the head. "How dare you make my son a captive? You cruel Monster!" shouted Oluwa as he beat up the Tortoise and chased him away. Rere promised never to disobey his parents ever again.

02 Why the Sea is Salty

Once, there were two brothers, one rich and the other poor. One day, the poor man went to borrow some meat from his brother. The selfish brother gave him a cow's hoof and said, "Give this to Hiysi." The poor man thanked his brother and went to the forest to meet Hiysi, the wood goblin. Hiysi ate the cow's hoof gladly. In turn Hiysi gifted the poorman his wish fulfilling millstone, warning him to remember the magic words—'Grind, my millstone' to start and 'enough and have done' to stop. The poor man happily went home. The millstone gave him whatever he wanted and he became rich. His selfish brother saw this and borrowed the millstone. He went into the deep sea and asked the millstone to grind salt. But, he didn't know how to stop it and the millstone grinded so much salt, that the boat sank. The greedy brother drowned with his boat but the millstone is still grinding salt in the sea.

03 Why the Sun Follows the Moon

A long, long time ago, Sun and Moon were a happy couple that lived with their children. One day while going to the market, Moon asked Sun to watch over their sleeping children and warned him not to go too near them as his heat might melt them. Sun stood by their side watching them.

Suddenly overwhelmed with fatherly love, he kissed them and lo! All of them melted. Out of fear, Sun went and hid in the forest. Moon returned back and saw her melted children. "God! My children have melted. I won't forgive you, Sun," she sobbed. After few days Sun came to meet Moon and they both quarrelled. Sun threw the vegetables on Moon's face in anger and she left him and went away. The children became stars. From then on, Moon has marks on her face and the Sun keeps chasing Moon to make peace again.

04 The Mighty

A huge tree grew in a dense forest. Its leafy branches
were the home of countless birds and provided shade
to passersby. The tree was very proud of its robust
size. A little plant grew by its side. It was like a
willow, bending with the slightest breeze. One
day, the big tree asked the plant, "Why don't
you make your roots firm like me? Every time
the wind blows, you keep swaying to and fro."
The plant smiled and said, "I'm safe this way."
Hearing it, the tree burst out laughing and said
tauntingly, "Ha! Ha! I see how safe you are. Even
a child can pluck you out."

A few days later a storm came and destroyed the
entire forest. Even the giant tree was uprooted but the
plant withstood the storm and continued to grow.

05 The Curse of the Chameleon

God saw that his beloved creation, the people had started
to look dull. There were scars of injuries here and there
on their bodies. So God called upon Chameleon and
said, "Take this parcel to my people on Earth."
Chameleon left with the parcel under his arms.
It was a hot day and Chameleon stopped to
drink some water and met his cousin, Snake.
Snake hated the people and knowing where
Chameleon was going, he decided to rob the
parcel. He took Chameleon home and treated
him to a delicious meal. As Chameleon dozed off
after the hearty meal, the snake quickly stole the
parcel and opened it. "Ha! These people will never
have these new skins," he smiled wickedly. When
Chameleon woke up and saw the gift in Snake's hand, he
pleaded to return it. But Snake refused. Fearing to encounter
God, Chameleon kept hiding beneath the leaves and trees. And till date
it keeps hiding.

06 Tenalirama Robs the Robbers' Labour

One night some thieves hid in Tenalirama's courtyard, intending to break into the house. Tenalirama sensed it and said aloud to his wife, "Put all the valuables into a box and hide it in the well in our courtyard. The town is under the threat of burglary." Tenali then dragged a huge box filled with garbage, dropped it into the well and went off to sleep. The thieves heard what he had said and tiptoed to the well. They started drawing out the water and poured into the nearby garden. But the water did not come down to the expected level. It was almost dawn and the thieves were very tired. Just then Tenalirama came out yawning and said, "Thank you for watering the plants in the garden!"

The thieves looked back and seeing Tenalirama ran out as fast as they could. Thus, with his wit, Tenalirama not only saved his valuables from being robbed but also got his garden irrigated free of cost.

07 The Clever Swan

Once, a flight of swans made their nests in a big banyan tree. One of the swans was very wise and far sighted. One day he noticed a twiner growing. He called his friends and said, "We need to destroy this twiner." The others laughed at his concern. Days passed and the twiner grew up the tree like a thick rope. One morning, a hunter came into the forest. He climbed up to the swans' nests with the help of the twiner and laid a trap. In the evening the swans returned to their nests and got trapped. As they shouted for help, the wise swan sang:

My warning fell on deaf ear
Why do you now fear?

The other swans pleaded him to save them. So they all decided to feign death. The next morning the hunter came and saw the swans. Thinking them to be dead, he threw them one by one onto the ground. As soon as the last of the swans was thrown, all the swans flew away together.

08 Heron and Humming Bird

Heron and Humming Bird were good friends. One day Humming Bird told Heron, "Wonder if there's enough fish to feed all our kinds. Why don't we have a race and decide who owns the fish." Heron agreed and they fixed up a four days race with the dead tree by the far away river as the target line. Humming Bird was small and fast while Heron was huge and slow. Humming Bird flew far ahead of Heron as Heron struggled, flapping his giant wings. Seeing Heron's slow pace, Humming Bird decided to take it easy and rested every night while Heron kept on flying all night long. Finally on the fourth day, when Humming Bird flew to the dead tree, he was shocked to see Heron perched on it and left, leaving the fish to Heron.

09 The Brahmin, the Tiger and the Jackal

Once a Brahmin saw a tiger trapped in a cage. "Kind Man, get me out of this cage. I'll be forever grateful to you," implored the tiger. The Brahmin took pity and opened the cage. As soon as the tiger was free, he pounced on the Brahmin saying, "Foolish man, I'm going to feed on you now." The frightened Brahmin pleaded for his life. The tiger growled and said,

"Ok, I'll spare you if only you can find three things that agree with whatever you say." The Brahmin set on his way and came across a tree, a buffalo and a road, but none of them agreed with him. Feeling sad, the Brahmin walked back to the tiger. On the way, he met a jackal. He tried to explain the entire story but the jackal failed to understand. He then took the jackal to the tiger, who decided to enact and show what had actually happened. As soon as the tiger went into the cage, the jackal bolted the door and said with a smile, "Your Majesty, this is where you deserve to be."

10 An Unpleasant Smell

Once, a rich moneylender had a tanner as his neighbour. Every day the tanner would be busy converting leather into hide by treating it with tannin. The strong odour of the tannin was unbearable for the moneylender. He went up to the tanner and offered to buy his house. The tanner smiled and said, "Do give me a week's time to wind up an important assignment." The moneylender readily agreed. After a week he came back to the tanner. Having no intentions of selling his house, the tanner made an excuse of his mother's arrival and asked the moneylender to wait for a month. The moneylender waited impatiently for the month to pass by. But after some days he got used to the smell and was no longer disturbed. So he forgot all about buying the tanner's house.

11 Why Turtles Live in Water

The turtles enjoyed living on the sands of the riverbank. All day long they would play in the golden sand and relax. One day some villagers caught a wise turtle. They took it to their chief. The chief looked at the turtle's huge size and wondered how to kill it. He then decided to break its shell. The turtle heard the chief and sang aloud:

Don't bash me with a stick
In vain will you become weak
Just drown me in the water
And then enjoy me with butter

The chief liked the turtle's advice and ordered his men to carry it to the river in a net. But as soon as they drowned the net, the turtle swam into the water and shouted out, "You foolish men, you've lost your bait." From then on the turtles decided to stay in water for safety.

12 Appearances are Deceptive

Kamya was a hard working ant. She always worked hard gathering food for her community. She ran all around the forest and collected a good stock of food. The only thing she needed to look around now was bits of sweetmeat which the younger ants enjoyed having. One day she saw a piece of cake lying under a tree. She hurried to get it. Suddenly she looked up and saw a pupa hanging from a branch. Not knowing what a pupa is, Kamya pitied its inactive state. After some days, Kamya came back to look for more pieces of sweetmeat. Suddenly she looked up and saw a beautiful brightly coloured butterfly. "Wow! What a beauty," she exclaimed. Sundari, the butterfly heard Kamya and said, "I'm the same creature whom you pitied the other day," and gracefully flew away.

13 The Crane's Walk

A crab lived with her son on the beach of a mighty blue sea. She enjoyed playing with her son on the golden sand and watching the sea waves. One day as the crab was watching her son play, she saw a crane walking gracefully with its long legs on the beach. The elegant gait of the crane caught the crab's attention and she thought, "How gracefully she's walking and here comes my son looking so shoddy, like a sack." She immediately told her son, "Try and walk straight." The little crab was surprised to hear his mother and said softly, "Mother, I don't know how to walk straight. Why don't you show me, maybe I'll learn then." The mother crab tried her level best to imitate the crane's walk but failed. Quite tired and frustrated with her failure to do so, she gave up her attempt and told her son,

"Leave it, child. Maybe we're born to walk sideways. It's nature's rule." The son smiled and started playing again.

14 The Dream Palace

King Krishnadevaraya once dreamt of a beautiful palace hanging in the air, full of all kinds of luxuries and desired to own such a palace. Everyone realised the king's stupidity but none dared to tell him. So the ministers sought Tenalirama's help to bring the king to his senses. One day an old man came crying to the king complaining that the king had looted his wealth in his dreams. Annoyed at the old man's words, the king said angrily, "Foolish man, how can a dream be a reality?" Hearing the king's words, Tenalirama at once revealed his identity and said, "Your Majesty, that's what the matter is. Your dream palace can never be a reality too." The king realised his foolishness and laughed.

15 Tiger Curse

Once, Ethoa, a brave warrior, decided to visit his sister Noh who lived in a distant village with her husband. It was a long journey and he had to pass through many jungles. When night dawned, Ethoa rested on the wide spread branches of a tree. After a while, Ethoa heard a tiger saying to the tree, "Come, let's go to the village and see Noh's new born son. It seems he would be killed by a tiger on his wedding day." Ethoa heard their conversation and rushed to meet Noh. He told Noh to consult him before her son's wedding and left. Years passed and the boy grew up to be a handsome young man. Noh fixed his wedding and invited Ethoa. All night long, Ethoa guarded his nephew. At dawn, the boy went out to the field and was attacked by a tiger. Ethoa saved his nephew and told everybody what he had heard years back. Hearing his uncle, the boy kicked the dead tiger's mouth. But alas! His leg got ripped with the tiger's tooth and he bled to death.

16 The Purse of Gold

A beggar found a leather purse containing hundred gold coins on the road. He picked it up and opened it. Suddenly he heard a merchant declaring a hundred gold coins for the one who finds his leather purse. The beggar was honest and decided to return the purse to its owner. He handed the purse to the merchant and asked for his reward. But the greedy merchant refused saying that the beggar had already fleeced him off a hundred gold coins as his purse contained two hundred gold coins and now it had only a hundred. The beggar took the matter to the court. The judge heard them and handing over the purse to the beggar saying. "Gentleman, this purse can't be yours as it has only a hundred gold coins. Yours had two hundred."

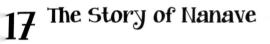

17 The Story of Nanave

The king of sharks transformed himself into a handsome man and married a beautiful girl. They had a son named Nanave who had the mark of a shark's mouth on his back. Advising his wife not to remove his feathered cape from their son's shoulders, the king left to meet his people. Nanave grew up to be a charming boy. Everyday he would disappear in the water for hours. Gradually the village fishermen started getting very few fish. So the village chief called everyone for a meeting and declared that they are under the spell of an evil spirit whom they need to find. He asked the villagers to walk over a stretch of leaves saying, "Humans will leave footprints but spirits won't." When Nanave's turn came, he slipped and everyone saw the shark's mark on his shoulder. As everyone chased him, Nanave jumped into the river and joined his father on the riverbed.

18 Why the Evergreen Never Loses its Needles

It was a cold winter morning. As every bird flew away to warmer lands, a little swallow repented, "Ptssh...I've broken my wing and can't fly." The swallow went to the birch, the oak and the willow trees seeking refuge, but they all refused. Quite frustrated, the swallow started flying aimlessly. Suddenly he heard a friendly voice, "Little bird, come and stay in my branches till spring comes and your friends are back." The swallow looked back and saw the kind spruce tree. "Oh! I'm so glad," thanked the swallow. The pine tree offered to protect them from the cold north winds and the juniper offered to feed the swallow with its berries. The other trees laughed at them for welcoming a stranger. One day, a strong gust of north wind came and destroyed all the green leaves of the birch, the oak and the willow. While their leaves lay scattered on the ground, the frost king spared the spruce, the pine and the juniper for their kindness. This is why they are evergreen.

19 Two Men Go on a Journey

Two friends once set off on a long journey. After a while, one of them started showing his true selfish colours. He insisted in having food and drink from his friend's supply. Before long, the food of the generous friend was finished. Now, when it was the turn of the other companion to share his food, he simply refused. The generous one had to sell all his possessions to buy food and drink and soon was left with nothing. He once again requested for food and this time his selfish friend said, "Take out your eyes and only then I'll give you food." The generous friend had no choice but obey. The cruel man left leaving behind his friend under a tree and left. Suddenly there appeared a large bird, which came and gave him some leaves. "Rub them on your eyes and you'll see again." When the man regained his vision, the bird quipped, "With your renewed vision, try to see the world as it is, for ignorance breeds trouble!"

20 What's for Dinner?

A cock lived in a small hut at the edge of a forest. He was hard working and led a happy life. A lazy fox and his old mother were his neighbours. One day the fox had nothing to eat and decided to kill the cock. "Mother, boil a pot of water while I go and bring our neighbour in a sack. We'll have him for dinner," said the fox and left. Finding the door ajar, the fox entered the cock's hut and hid himself. As soon as the cock walked in, the fox pounced on him and tied him up in a sack. As he carried him home, the cock cut open the sack and jumped out, leaving a stone behind. The fox happily went home thinking of a delicious meal. But alas! The moment he dropped the stone, the boiling water splashed on their faces, which blinded both mother and son. The cock lived peacefully thereafter.

21 The Lad Who Made the Princess Tell the Truth

Once, a king had a daughter who was a big fibber. Tired of her lies, the king declared that whosoever could outwit his daughter in telling fibs and make her speak the truth, would marry his daughter and have half of his kingdom. Young men from every nook and corner of the kingdom tried, but were unsuccessful. Then one day, three brothers tried their luck. When the two elder brothers failed, the younger brother came forward. He narrated the princess an incident where he claimed to have seen the queen giving the king a big hit which made figs fall out of the king's hair. The princess heard him and shouted in anger, "My father never grew figs on his head." The lad smiled at the princess's true words. He thus won both the princess's hand and half of the kingdom.

22 How Men Lost Their Tails

Early men were born with tails and had great difficulty in moving around as they used to tread on each other's tails. Once the Great God Kittung went to a crowded fair and looked around for some good tobacco. As he looked through the stalls, someone stepped on his tail. "Ouch… Leave my tail," screamed the Great God and fell headlong on a stone, breaking two of his teeth. Seing him fall, everyone laughed. Kittung lost his temper and decided to teach them a lesson. In a fit of anger, he lifted his tail, swept it across forcefully and laid a curse on all mankind. The Great God Kittung's tail became the sago palm and the other men's tails became grass. From then on men never had tails.

23 The Palm Reader

Hari Prasad was a renowned palm reader. People would flock to him from all over to get their palms read and know about their future, not knowing that Hari Prasad only looked into the fine lines on their palms and said some general things, common to all. Some of his predictions came true and people gradually developed blind faith in his prophecies and came to him in large numbers. Their folly made Hari Prasad smile. One day, as Hari Prasad was sitting down in his shop and reading the palms of his customers, his neighbour's son came running into his shop and said, "Uncle, some thieves have broken into your house. Please hurry home, else the thieves will flee." Hari Prasad dropped everything and started running towards his house, leaving the people to wonder why he had not prophesised his own future.

24 The Travellers

Three young merchants had heard stories of people trading overseas and prospering. "Let's go to a distant land and try our luck too," suggested one of the merchants. All three agreed and they decided to go on a long voyage to trade in faraway lands and become rich. They sailed for days together in a small ship and stopped at several cities to trade. But unfortunately, they could not earn much and spent more than what they had earned. "Gosh! We've travelled so far in vain.

We couldn't make any profit," said one of the merchants. One day while they were marooned on a coastal town, they saw a huge ship in the distant sea. "Wish we could own such a ship," thought the merchants and watched as the ship turned in their direction. They waited for a long time but as the ship came nearer, they saw that it was only logs of wood tied together for rafting. They realised that they have wasted their time in watching the ship and similarly their money in their fruitless voyages and decided to return home.

25 Lion's Share

A lion, an ass and a fox once made an agreement to help each other in hunting. They decided that the ass would lure the prey, the fox would chase them to the lion who would finally kill it. Quite hesitant, the ass asked, "Did we do the right thing?" "Oh yes! Think of the huge portion we'll have out of the hunt," said the fox. So the next day the trio set out to hunt as decided. By evening, they had a huge collection and returned to the lion's den. The lion asked the ass to divide the hunt. Thinking it to be an honour, the ass gladly made three equal shares. This annoyed the lion and he killed the ass. The lion then asked the fox to divide. The fox seeing the ass's plight, made two unequal halves, one big and the other small. He gave the bigger share to the lion and this pleased the lion. But the fox decided never to be a lion's hunting partner.

26 The Bags of Pebbles

Once upon a time, a very wealthy farmer fell seriously ill. Thinking that he was about to die, he called his three sons and divided his property among them. However, to his sons' surprise the old man recovered from his illness and continued to live for several years afterwards. Now that the sons had received their share of wealth, their conduct had changed. They neglected their father and even behaved rudely with him. The old man was deeply hurt by his sons' behaviour. One day, on the advice of his friend, the old man quietly brought two bags full of gravel in his room. "Tell your sons that I have repaid my long-standing debt to you. But tell them not to touch these bags as long as you are alive", said his friend. When the sons came to know that the bags contained a lot of money, they started caring for their father again. It was only after the old man's death that they discovered in dismay that the bags contained only small pebbles.

27 The Apple Tree

There was an old apple tree in a farmer's orchard. It no longer bore any fruits but was the home of many birds, grasshoppers and other creatures. Deciding to use the wood to make some furniture, the farmer one day started cutting the tree with his axe. "Please, don't make us homeless," pleaded the creatures that lived on the tree. "I'll sing to you," promised the cuckoo but the farmer continued axing the tree ignoring their pleas. Suddenly he noticed a beehive in the hollow of the trunk. He tasted a bit of honey and thought, "Hmm… the tree is not that useless. I should not cut it." So the farmer got the honey out of the beehive and left.

28 The Trial

A young man was asked to pass the trial of being immersed three days in water to marry a merchant's daughter whom he loved. On the third day he saw a fire atop the distant hill and raised his hands towards the flames. Considering this to be a breach of rule, the merchant refused his daughter's hand and asked him to hold a banquet as compensation. On a judge's advice the young man made saltless food and served, keeping the salt separately. When the merchant complained about saltless food, the young man said, "If I can warm my hands from a fire so distant, can't you taste salt kept so near?" The merchant felt embarrassed and agreed for the marriage.

Contents

The Story of the Month: Kodilikane

The Story of the Month

Kodilikane

01 Kodilikane

Kodilikane was a very beautiful girl. The other girls in the village were very jealous of Kodilikane because all the boys admired her. One day, her friends decided to play a prank on her. "We have all thrown our precious jewels in that lake and look how they are sparkling under the morning sun!" they said. Kodilikane believed her friends, and threw her beaded necklace and her glass bangles into the lake. "Oh, what a fool Kodilikane is!" they said clapping their hands as the poor girl's eyes welled up with tears.

Kodilikane rushed to the lake and began a frantic search for her necklace and the bangles. Suddenly, she saw a weird creature pop out of the water. It was an old woman with one leg and one eye. "Oh, don't cry like a baby!" shouted the old woman. "Who… who are you?" asked Kodilikane nervously. "I was once as beautiful as you. But, my friends played a nasty trick on me and threw me into this lake which belongs to the demon, Dino and since then, I have been caged here."

As the old lady narrated her sad tale, tears rolled down Kodilikane's white cheeks. "Nobody has ever shed a tear for me. Why are you wasting your precious tears for me?" asked the woman. "Because I feel pity for you and pray to god that he may help you!" replied Kodilikane. "Oh, you have such a warm heart!" replied the woman, "maybe I should help you."

Kodilikane then narrated her story and told the woman that her friends had played a prank on her. "Oh, don't worry young lady, I will adorn you with the costliest diamonds and give you the most beautiful clothes!" The old lady chanted some magical lines and a new dress with precious jewels appeared. Kodilikane adorned herself and looked at her reflection in the water. "Is this really me?" asked an astonished Kodilikane who looked like a beautiful princess.

When Kodilikane reached home, all the villagers gathered at her house to see the beautiful young girl. "Oh, she looks like a thousand roses!' remarked one of her neighbours. "She is fit to be the bride of our prince!" said another. Meanwhile, Kodilikane told her friends about her meeting with the old lady.

Her friends also went to the lake and called out for the old lady. "Here I am," said the old woman in a croaky voice and came out of the lake. The girls shrieked in fright and were about to run away when the old lady said, "Don't you want those precious jewels and that lovely costume!" "Yes, we do!" replied the girls and stepped into the water. "Ha- ha-ha ha!" laughed the old lady menacingly and chanted some magical lines. "Now look at your reflection in the water!" she told them. "Oh no!" screamed one of the girls when she saw her charred complexion. "Oh no, I have become bald!" cried another girl. "And look at my eyes, they are squinted now!" lamented another girl. "Well, this is your punishment for being so nasty to poor little Kodilikane," said the old lady and disappeared. When the girls returned home, all the villagers laughed at them. Meanwhile, the news of the beautiful Kodilikane reached the prince. He arrived at the village and asked for her hand in marriage. Kodilikane agreed and soon she became the queen of the kingdom.

02 The Buffalo Boy and the Banyan Tree

A long time ago in Vietnam, there lived a poor buffalo boy named Cuoi. Every morning he went out with the buffaloes to the rice fields. He bathed them and fed them. For his services, the buffalo owner paid him a paltry sum at the end of the month.

One day, while returning home from the fields, Cuoi saw a wounded dog wreathing in pain. "Oh poor dog!" cried Cuoi and rushed to help him. He carried the dog to a lake nearby and washed its wounds. But the blood from the wound didn't stop oozing. Suddenly he recalled his grandmother telling him once that such wounds could be treated with banyan leaves. Coui saw a banyan tree near the lake and quickly climbed its branches and plucked some fresh leaves. He chewed them and made a thick paste, which he applied on the dog's wound. And lo! The wound dried up and healed after some time. Happily, Cuoi rushed home and told his mother of the miracle. Since then the people of Vietnam have adopted the custom of treating their wounds with the paste of banyan leaves.

03 How Philippines was formed

The people of Philippines have an interesting tale about how their country was formed.

There was a time, when the universe had no planets. It was made up of the limitless sky, a boundless sea and a large bird, which flew constantly between the two. Tired of his journey between the sea and the sky and unable to find a place to rest, the bird thought it wise to begin an argument between the sky and the sea. He told the sky that the sea wants to devour it with its gigantic waves and to the sea he said that the sky wanted to overcome it gradually. Furious, the sea and the sky began to fight. The sea raised itself so high that the sky was threatened that it might indeed get devoured very soon. The sky on its part lashed out with bursts of thunder and lightning. However, the sea continued raising its height. The sky then began throwing soil and rocks on the sea and soon, a huge pile of rocks was formed in the sea. With time this pile changed into the seven thousand islands, which constitute the land of Philippines.

04 The Clever Thief

Once there lived a very smart thief in Saudi Arabia. One day, he was crossing the border with a donkey whose back was heavily laden with straw. Suspicious of his activities, the policemen at the border stopped him. "We want to search the donkey!" they said. They rummaged through the stack of straw but did not find anything. "I am just an innocent farmer taking my donkey home. How can I hide anything valuable!" said the clever thief. This way, every day for ten years the man arrived with a huge stack of straw piled on the donkey's back and crossed the border. The policeman who guarded the border firmly believed that the man was lying and was up to some mischief.

Years later, when the policeman retired from his job he met the thief one day and asked, "I beg you, please tell me. What were you smuggling in every day across the border?" The clever thief replied, "No valuables Sir, just donkeys!"

05 Abdullah's Gold

Abdullah was a rich merchant, but very stingy. He had lots of money and jewellery but all he did was open his treasure chest every day and stare at the valuables. "There goes the miser!" the people of the town said. "These greedy people are eyeing my treasure!" reasoned Abdullah. "Maybe I should hide it somewhere safe." That night when everybody was sleeping, Abdullah went to a well in front of his house and threw the treasure chest into it. "Nobody will ever suspect that the valuables are here!" he thought. However, unable to resist himself, Abdullah went to the well to check his valuables every day and the people soon understood what was going on.

One day Abdullah's treasure was stolen and he wailed, "I am ruined now!" "Why don't you throw a box of stones into that well and stare at it!" joked Abdullah's neighbour. "How dare you make fun of me!" said an angry Abdullah. "Well, when you had the treasure all you did was stare at it, so you can continue doing the same now!" explained the man and walked away.

06 Why Dogs Chase Cats

Once, a dog and a cat lived together in a cave. One morning, the dog got a bag full of meat. "Please cook this meat for lunch!" said the dog to the cat and then went out for an urgent errand. When the cat opened the bag and saw the meat, she thought, "Let me have some meat and I'll cook the rest for Doggy Dear!" She chomped on the meat leisurely. It was delicious! She wanted to keep some for her friend, but could not resist and soon finished all that was there in the bag. In the afternoon when the dog returned, the cat made a fine excuse, "Oh, I was just about to cook when a crow came and flew away with the bag!" The dog however understood that something was wrong. He got another bag of meat and asked the cat to cook it while he went and completed his work. This time the dog hid himself in the cupboard and watched the cat. The cat laughed gleefully and began eating the meat. "You wicked creature!" yelled the dog and began chasing the cat and ever since dogs have been chasing cats.

07 The Instructor

Once, a young boy eager to learn sword playing enrolled himself in the school of a famous swordsman. However, instead of being taught anything about swords, the young learner was asked to cook, mop floors and wash clothes. Quite disturbed, he approached his instructor one morning, "Sir, why aren't you teaching me anything about sword playing?" he asked.

The next day, the teacher came from behind and hit the boy on his head. The boy was taken aback. Such surprise attacks became a regular affair, until one day when the instructor came to hit the boy, the boy skillfully dodged and managed to escape the blow. "Bravo young boy!" exclaimed the instructor and left. After a few days, the young boy tried the same tactic with his teacher. He stepped forward stealthily and was about to hit his master when the expert swordsman ducked his head and hit the boy instead. "Sword playing is not about learning the art of wielding your sword, but about understanding what's on your opponent's mind and countering that skillfully," said the instructor.

08 The Priest and the Three Crooks

One day three crooks saw an old priest carrying a healthy lamb. "Oh, that lamb would taste delicious when cooked!" they thought. The three got together and chalked a plan. After a while, the first man approached the priest, "Oh, it's such a shame that a religious man like you should eat a dog!"

"This is not a dog, it's a lamb!" said the priest. "Oh, but I can see that it's a dog!" persisted the wicked man. The priest did not reply but walked on instead. Soon the second crook approached him and said, "Why do you want to kill this innocent deer!" The priest now realised that something was amiss. Soon the third crook came and said, "Please, let this helpless foal go!" The priest now fully understood their plan and replied sternly, "This lamb is my pet and if you think I am foolish enough to believe you crooks then you are mistaken!" So wise men say, "Don't give in to what wicked men say, for they will always try to distort the truth and cause harm!"

09 How the Moon Was Created

Long ago when God had just created the universe, there was no moon, only the sun. People did not know what night or darkness was. The sun gave them light throughout the day. The men and women worked endlessly and with lack of sleep or rest, they began falling ill. God who was watching from above pondered, "Oh, my people are falling sick, I should do something to give them some rest!" So God asked the sun to set so that night could follow. However, as soon as night was created and darkness spread everywhere, chaos ensued. The people couldn't see anything and fell into ditches, knocked against each other and got hurt. "I have to find a way to help those men on earth!" cried out God, seeing the result of his creations. He thought long and hard and then created the moon. "My dear earthlings, I have created something like the sun but with less light. It will give you enough light for you to see in the dark!"

Ever since the moon has been shining softly at night.

10 The Leap

Once there lived a man who was always lying. One day, he went to visit a friend. During the course of conversation he claimed to have travelled the world. "Have you seen the pyramids?" asked his friend. "The pyramids! Ha! Of course I have seen them," said the man proudly. He then boasted of having climbed Mount Everest and of having dinner with the queen of England, proclaiming that he was a famous magician. After a while, a group of villagers came to meet the man. "We have heard that you are a famous man, why don't you tell us about some of your achievements too?" they said. The man then began spinning another colourful yarn of lies. "I must tell you about my greatest achievement!" he announced. "I once jumped from the roof of one building to another which was ten metres apart!" "Why don't you jump between these two buildings which are barely five metres apart!" challenged one villager. "I need to have a quick bath. I'll be back soon," said the man and ran away from the village.

11 The Little Men

The tribes of Bastar in the state of Chhattisgarh have a fascinating tale on how people grew taller. They believe that when God had created the universe, the sky, the sun and the moon were so close to earth that they often knocked against the human beings. So everybody had to bend while walking. One day, an old lady was cleaning her courtyard when she saw thick rain clouds gather above her. As the clouds became bigger they brushed against her and she had to bend further. Unable to bear the weight on her shoulders, she toppled after a while. She picked up her broom and hit the cloud hard with it. "Go away you giant!" she yelled. At once the sky and the clouds began moving up and went so high that no man could ever touch the sky again. Since then God decided to make men taller. Now they could walk the earth with their heads held high!

12 Coyote and the Columbia

A baby coyote once lost his way while wandering through a forest of Columbia. Tired after the long and frantic search, he sat down and started crying, "Dear God, please help me find my way back home!" The God's took pity and created a thick black cloud in the sky. "Yippee rain clouds!" cried the coyote. Soon more clouds came along and little drops of rain fell on the coyote's furry head. "I want more rain!" he cried looking at the sky. The Gods who were watching from above agreed to the coyote's wish. The rains came lashing on the entire forest and slowly flooded the entire valley. The coyote was swept away by the force of the water. "This is so much fun!" he cried out while being tossed and turned by the waves. As he flowed across the valley, he suddenly saw something and jumped. It was his mother! The coyote swam to the banks and hugged his mother while the flooded river streamed on and on.

13 The Wise Donkey

Here's a famous Indian folktale on how a meek creature taught his powerful enemy a lesson. One day, while roaming the forests, a timid little donkey suddenly saw a big lion standing before him. "You sure will make a delicious meal!" said the lion smacking his lips. He slowly inched forward towards the meek donkey that was about to bolt, when suddenly the donkey got an idea. "Sir, before you eat me I have something to tell you!" said the donkey and continued, "a sharp thorn has been wedged in my feet since morning. If not removed, I fear it will prick your throat when you eat me!" "I will do anything for a delicious meal, my dear," said the lion and brought his face close to the donkey's feet to have a look. But lo! The donkey gave one forceful kick on his face and galloped away. "I should have known!" moaned the mighty lion upon seeing his delicious meal disappearing before his eyes.

14 The Wise Old Rabbit

Once, under a big apple tree, there lived a tiger who never shared the fruits of the tree with the other animals. One day, a wise old rabbit called an urgent meeting. "I have devised a plan to teach the tiger a lesson," he announced. "Tomorrow each one of you must come near the apple tree and when I say, 'the big wind is coming,' you should run helter- skelter and make lot of noise." The next morning, the rabbit went up to the tiger and shouted, "Tiger! Tiger! Please wake up!" "How dare you wake me up!" growled the tiger. "Oh! The big wind is coming and is going to blow us all away!" As soon as all the animals heard this, they began running here and there and there was a commotion. "What should I do now," said the tiger anxiously. "Let me tie you to the tree trunk with a thick rope, so that you are not blown away!" explained the rabbit. As soon as the tiger was tied to the tree trunk, all the other animals rushed to the apple tree and began eating the apples.

15 The Proud Fox's Tail

Once upon a time there lived a fox who was very proud of his long bushy tail. "Look at my gorgeous tail," he boasted. One day while taking a stroll, the fox got trapped in a hunter's trap. After trying for a long time, he managed to free himself, but his precious tail got stuck in the steel frames of the snare. The fox made one last effort and pulled so hard that his tail snapped off. "My tail is no more!" he wailed in dismay. "What will I tell my friends!" he thought. On the way back he thought of a plan to convince his friends. That evening when his friends saw him they jeered at the fox, "Where is the bushiest part of your body?" "Oh I had it cut. It's the latest fad!" the fox said confidently. "When one loses his tail in a trap it indeed becomes a fashion!" joked another friend, holding out the fox's tail as proof.

16 Tenalirama and the Jinx

One day in the kingdom of Vijaynagar, a rumour spread that a man named Ramaya was bringing ill luck to the kingdom. "Don't go near him, or look into his eyes!" said the people.

When King Krishnadevaraya got the news he called Ramaya to his court. "I am a poor old man, Sir. How can I bring ill luck!" pleaded Ramaya with tears in his eyes. "We shall know soon enough!" said the king sternly. That evening when the King was about to eat his food, he saw a fly in his food. "This has never happened before. I am convinced that it is Ramaya who has brought me such misfortune," complained the king and ordered his soldiers to hang Ramaya. When Ramaya was being taken to the gallows he met Tenalirama. He appealed to Tenalirama for forgiveness. Tenalirama rushed to the king and said, "Sir, I have an appeal. If Ramaya has brought you ill luck, how are you any better, because you have brought him death?" The king was filled with a deep sense of shame and immediately forgave Ramaya.

17 Why the Opossum Has a Pouch?

An opossum is a soft furry animal with a little pouch in its belly. However, opossums did not have a pouch when God first created them. The legend goes that long time ago there lived a mama opossum with her six babies. One day while she was playing with her babies, a wicked bat swooped down and picked up all the babies and flew away. Mama opossum searched everywhere till she came to a dark cave where she heard the helpless cry of her babies. "Someone, please save us!" they were shouting. Mama opossum rushed to meet the wise terrapin who was her friend. "I have a plan," said the terrapin. He quickly got a knife and cut a portion of the opossum's belly and made a pouch there. At night when the bat went out of the cave to look for his food, mama opossum quickly went in and called out to her babies. "Come, come hide here!" she said to them pointing to her pouch and ran away with her babies hiding in her belly. Ever since, mama opossums have carried their little ones in their pouch.

18 The Origin of Thunder and Lightning

A Cambodian legend explains the origin of thunder and lightning.

Long ago there lived a hermit who wanted to pass on his magical powers to one of his diligent students. However, among his students, he couldn't judge whether it was the goddess Moni Mekhala or the giant Ream Eyso who was more deserving and capable. So the hermit put forward a challenge. "Whosoever brings me a glass full of morning dew first will get my magical powers!" Ream gathered as many leaves as he could and let the droplets of dew slide from each leaf into his glass. Moni Mekhala kept a handkerchief on the grass overnight and early next morning squeezed the dew into a glass and gave it to the hermit. "You deserve the magical inheritance, Moni," said the hermit. The hermit's magic had the power to perform many tricks and whosoever possessed it, became the most powerful person on earth. Jealous of Moni's win, Ream Eyso attacked her. Moni used the magical powers to create thunder and lightning and defeated Ream Eyso.

19 The Tale of Two Sons

A businessman had two sons. He always showered the younger son with affection and gifts while he neglected the elder son. When the boys grew up, the father divided his share of business between the two sons. This time too, he was partial to the younger son and gave him a profitable share of the business, confident of his success.

As the months passed, the elder son worked hard day and night and proved his ability. His business prospered whereas the younger son spent all his money foolishly and was soon bankrupt.

The businessman was filled with grief that his younger son had dashed all his hopes. "I gave him the best of education and all that he asked for and he let me down?" the businessman complained angrily to the elder son. "Father, it is you who is responsible for what has happened. It is because of the undue love and money you gave him that my brother could never realise the worth of money and hard work," said the elder son.

20 The Wooden God

Raju's family was very religious and performed all kinds of rituals and fasts to please God. Their deity was a wooden God called Jagannath. Inspite of their prayers, Raju's family remained poor while the others flourished. But Raju did not believe in idle prayers. He worked hard in the fields and earned whatever he could to feed his family. One day Raju's parents had gone for a wedding to another village near the coast. There was a terrible storm and Raju's parents lost their way. The following day, the authorities informed Raju that his parents could not be found. Raju was heartbroken. After that day, Raju's family realised that it was no use praying to a blind wooden deity without doing one's duty for God helps those who help themselves. Raju's parents returned safely after a few days but from then on, Raju's family also worked in the fields like he did.

21 Painting with a Difference

Once King Krishnadevrai hired a famous painter to fill the walls of his new mansion with paintings. After the work was completed, the king accompanied by his ministers took a round of the mansion and greatly appreciated the paintings. Suddenly, Tenalirama noticed a painting that was painted sideways and drew the king's attention to it saying, "Your Highness, I can't see what is on the other side." The king laughed and said, "You must be dreaming, Tenali." Tenali nodded his head and smiled. After a month or so, Tenali announcing that he had developed interest in painting, replaced the old paintings in the mansion with new ones. A week later, when the king came to inspect Tenali's paintings, he became angry for he could see nothing but limbs and pieces. On being questioned, Tenali asked the king to imagine the remaining portions to be on the other side. The angry king remembered his own words and kept silent.

22 How the First House Was Built

When the world had just been created, humans were as small as rabbits and lived under trees. It was a tough life for them as they had to survive the bitter cold of winter, the raging heat of summer and the rainy season. Gradually, humans started living in burrows but that did not solve their problems either as wild animals would often attack them. One day, the humans held a meeting to discuss their problems. They finally decided to make a tree house. So they made an umbrella out of leaves and branches and lived under them. Life became a bit better but since the houses did not have any walls, they continued to shiver in the winters and sweat in the summers. Finally, one day, the humans discovered how to make walls. This was the start of the creation of real houses. Soon, life improved a lot for the humans and they lived happily and comfortably. They built their houses close to each other so that they could live as a community.

23 The Crafty Doctor

Once an old woman lost her eyesight completely. She went to a doctor and requested him to cure her. The doctor took advantage of the woman's blindness and began stealing valuables from her house when he went to visit her. Finally, when there was nothing left to steal, he decided to cure the woman's eyes and then demanded a big payment. The woman soon discovered that all her valuables were gone and it dawned on her that nobody else, but the doctor could have stolen them. The next day when the doctor arrived, she refused to pay him saying that she had lost her eyesight once again. The doctor was furious and took the matter to the court. When the judge questioned the woman, she said, "Your honour, I'm not lying. When I could see everything, there were lots of precious things in my house but now, when the doctor says I'm cured, I cannot see any of the valuables that I had." The judge agreed that the woman was still blind and let her go.

24 Paul Sot Guards the Door

Paul Sot's mother had to go to the market so she asked him to guard the door. Paul Sot grew tired of waiting for her and started to worry. "How can I leave the door. Mom has told me to guard it," he wondered. So Paul took the door off its hinges and put it on his back. Then he went out to look for his mother. On the way, Paul Sot saw some robbers running with a sack. Paul was frightened and quickly climbed up a tree with the door! The thieves stopped below the tree and began counting their money. This is for you, this for you…" Paul heard the chief robber saying. "What about me?" Paul uttered from above. The robbers looked around in confusion and fear. They were convinced there was a devil around. Leaving the sack full of loot below the tree, they ran as fast as possible. Paul Sot climbed down the tree with the door, picked up the sack of money and took it home where his mother was eagerly waiting for him.

25 Learning to Act

Once there lived a brilliant student in China. Not satisfied with his knowledge, he wanted to acquire more experience. So he went to a famous teacher. He fell down at the teacher's feet and requested him to teach him. The master smiled and asked his assistant to bring two cups of tea. Lifting the big pot of tea, the teacher began to pour tea into the student's cup. Much to the student's amazement, he continued to pour till the tea started overflowing out of the cup and into the saucer. Soon, the tea spilled onto the floor. The student was startled, "Master, the cup cannot hold any more tea." The master smiled and stopped pouring more tea. Then he said, "In the same way, I want you to know that you've learnt enough. You must put your knowledge into practice, otherwise it will be wasted like this tea is. The student realised the importance of the master's words and returned home a wiser man.

26 The Elephant's Nose

Long time ago, the elephant's nose was merely the size of a boot until a very curious baby elephant changed everything. This little baby elephant had an inquisitive nature and would keep asking all sorts of questions.

One day he wanted to find out what crocodiles like to eat. Not knowing whom to approach, he went to the wise kolokolo bird and asked, "Can you help me find out what the crocodiles eat?" "Go to the green Limpopo River and find out," suggested the kolokolo bird.

So the baby elephant trudged to the riverside. Just then, a crocodile had lifted its head out of the water and was looking around hungrily.

"Hey, I've been looking for you. Tell me what do you eat?" the baby elephant shouted excitedly on seeing the crocodile.

"Come here and I shall tell you," said the crocodile slyly.

As the elephant went near, the crocodile caught him by his little nose. The elephant pulled while the crocodile too pulled and pulled the elephant's nose which kept on stretching. "Crashhhh…!" the elephant fell down on his big back.

By now, his nose had become so long that he could swish it around.

Ever since then the elephant roams around with a looooong nose.

27 The Favour

Once there lived a wolf called Bablu in the mountainous regions of India. He was very selfish and only thought of himself. None of the other animals in the forest liked him. One day, while Bablu was gulping down a hen that he had hunted, a small bone suddenly got stuck in his throat. Bablu coughed and coughed till he went red. He found it difficult to breathe and pleaded with all the other animals to help him take the bone out. At last, a crane took pity on the wolf and offered to help him. Bablu lay on his side and opened his jaws wide. The crane entered its long neck inside the wolf's throat and "Pluck!" it took out the small bone with its long beak. The wolf heaved a sigh of relief. When the crane asked Bablu for a reward, he grinned and replied. "You should be thankful that I did not harm your neck." The crane was disappointed and decided never to help wolves ever again.

28 The 'Groom'ed Horse

Once a rich farmer called Lakshman Singh, owned a very attractive horse named Chetak and was very proud of him.

One day Laxman hired Lalu, a new groom for Chetak. "You must take special care of my horse for he is very dear to me," Laxman told Lalu. As asked, Lalu took good care of Chetak, washing him every morning and brushing his coat till it shone. But Laxman Singh noticed that his horse didn't look happy and active as before. Worried at Chetak's changed behaviour, Laxman decided to find out the cause. A few days later,

Laxman discovered sackful of oats hidden in the tank behind the stable. At once he called Lalu and said angrily, "You cheat, I'm sure you wanted to sell off those good oats and starve my dear Chetak." He immediately dismissed Lalu and himself looked after Chetak.

29 The Jester and the Straw Root

Gopal the jester was very poor and lived with his wife in a mud hut which had a straw roof. His wife often nagged him saying, "The straw is getting really thin. It'll leak if it rains." Tired of her nagging, Gopal decided to do something about it. He invited the king to his house on Kartik Puja and made arrangements for the king to sit on the rooftop. When the king arrived, Gopal took him to the rooftop. The king was shocked to see such impudence. Sensing the king's anger, Gopal said humbly, "Where else will I make you sit in a mud hut?" The king understood Gopal's need and changed his hut into a bungalow.

30 Qui Jun and the Arrogant Monk

Qui Jun, the village chief, once went to visit Shan, the monk of the village monastery. Shan was ill famous for his pride and so Qui Jun decided to teach the arrogant monk a lesson. He went to meet the monk in the monastery. The proud monk did not greet or welcome Qui Jun but was very warm towards another visitor, an army officer and greeted him with a smile. Seeing his behaviour, Qui Jun thought, "Hmm...he's not the same with all," and asked the monk the reason behind it. "Oh, my actions are just the opposite of my thoughts," said the monk wearing a sly smile. Hearing his reply, Qui Jun hit the monk hard on his head with a stick. "Ouch... why have you done this to me?" cried Shan in anger. "My actions too means the opposite. This means that I'm not beating you," replied Qui Jun. The monk realised his folly and became humble henceforth.

31 Sound Advice

In a village, lived two brothers—the elder was wise and the younger was quite foolish. One day, the younger brother was working in the garden with his new spade when his brother called him to have lunch. "Wait a minute. I'll just hide my spade behind the hedges and come," shouted the younger one. "Why do you have to shout and tell where you've hidden the new spade. Anyone can hear you. What is meant for my ears should be heard by me alone," rebuked the elder brother. "Very well, brother. I'll remember that in future," said the younger one. After lunch when he returned to the garden, he found his spade was stolen and realised his folly.

Contents

The Story of the Month: Anansi, Firefly and Tiger

The Story of the Month

Anansi, Firefly and Tiger

01 Anansi, Firefly and Tiger

Once there lived a spider called Anansi. He was always in search of eggs and never missed any chance to steal them.

One day, a new firefly entered the forest. Anansi quickly became friendly with him. A few days later, the firefly invited Anansi to go egg-hunting with him. "Come to my house in the evening if you want to go with me. It's going to be fun."

Anansi had just been waiting for such an opportunity. He readily agreed to go with the firefly.

When it grew dark, Anansi and the firefly went out into the fields. Whenever the firefly opened his wings a little, his light illuminated the eggs lying hidden in the grass. At once, Anansi would grab the eggs and yell, "That's mine! I saw it first!" The two searched for eggs thus the rest of the evening. Anansi was so greedy and so rude that he took all the eggs, and the firefly had none.

Finally, the firefly said to Anansi, "Goodbye, I'm going home."

Now Anansi was left all alone in the dark. He had no idea how to return home. As he tried to find his way in the dark, he bumped into a house. Since he had no idea whose house it was, he quickly thought of a plan. "Grandfather, please open the door. Help me, please," Anansi called out.

A deep, gruff voice answered from within "Who is that?" "It's your grandson, Anansi," replied Anansi.

The next moment, a tiger's head leapt out of the door. "Oh, come in, grandson. How I've missed you!" said the tiger.

The tiger knew he had no grandsons. Anansi had fooled him many times in the past. The tiger thought this was a good opportunity to teach Anansi a lesson.

So Anansi the spider went inside the house where the tiger's wife and children were hungrily eating eggs. "Grandson, you can stay here for the night," said the tiger to Anansi. Greedy Anansi had seen some eggs left inside the kettle. His mouth watered at the sight. When the others were busy talking, the clever tiger had quietly put in a lobster into the kettle, but Anansi had not seen it.

When everyone had gone to sleep, Anansi quietly crept into the kettle to steal the eggs. But, to his shock, the lobster pinched him hard. Anansi's loud cry woke up the tiger family. "What happened, grandson? Are you alright?"

"Uh, grandfather, a dog-flea just bit me," said Anansi, trembling with fear.

"There are no dog-fleas in our house. You must be dreaming," said the tiger's wife in anger. "Go to sleep, grandson."

A few minutes later, Anansi again tried to grab an egg from the kettle and once again, the lobster pinched him hard. This time the tiger had caught the spider red-handed.

"How dare you steal our eggs? I knew you would be up to some mischief as usual," saying this, the tiger roared and tried to jump on Anansi. The terrified spider raced out of the door and never dared to play tricks on the tiger again.

Also, whenever Anansi went to the firefly's house, his wife would tell him that the firefly was not at home. Without the firefly's help, Anansi was never able to find that field where all the eggs were hidden.

Anansi's greed had left him without friends.

02 Tenalirama and the Brinjal

Once, King Krishnadevaraya invited his courtiers to a feast in which a special brinjal was to be served. Tenalirama's wife insisted on tasting the brinjals after hearing so much about it. So, one night, Tenali quietly plucked a few brinjals from the King's garden.

Tenali's wife did not want their son to miss the wonderful taste of the vegetable. But Tenali feared that the son might tell others about it so he thought of an idea. He poured water on his son who was sleeping on the roof. "Let's go inside. It's raining," said Tenali. Tenali changed the boy's clothes and then gave him the brinjal to eat. The next day, the King's gardener told the king about the missing brinjals. The king knew that only Tenali could dare to do such a thing. But knowing that Tenali was too clever, he called Tenali's son. The boy admitted that he had eaten delicious brinjals the previous night when it was raining heavily. "I think the boy must have eaten the brinjal in his sleep. We had clear weather last night," said an amused King and let the boy go.

03 The Mouse Who Lived in a Lion's Cave

A little mouse once lived in a lion's cave. At first the mouse was very scared of the lion. But slowly, she stopped fearing the lion, and one day, she climbed his back while the lion was sleeping. This awakened the lion and he was furious. The terrified mouse pleaded for her life promising to help the lion in need.

The lion laughed loudly at this and allowed the mouse to go warning her to be careful in future. One day, the lion walked into a hunter's trap. He tried in vain to get out of the net. The mouse, who was passing by, saw the lion and remembered her promise. She made a big hole in the net with her teeth for the lion to come out.

The lion thanked the mouse for saving his life and said, "You can live on my back, little mouse."

04 The Red-and-Blue Coat

Once there were two friends. Their houses stood opposite each other and a small path separated their farms. One day, a man in the village decided to play a trick on them. He wore a two-collar coat that was red on one side and blue on the other. Then the man walked along the path between the two houses and made a noise so that the two men would notice him. Later, one friend said to the other, "Did you see the beautiful red coat that man was wearing?" "Wasn't it a blue coat?" said the other friend. "No. It was clearly red. But I remember it was blue," replied the other friend angrily. Thus, a heated argument started between the two friends. The man who played the trick saw them and laughed out saying, "Both of you are right in your own way. My coat is red on one side and blue on the other. You are fighting because you saw only what could be seen from your side."

05 How Stars Came into Being

Once there was an old man who smoked tobacco in terracotta or clay pipes called pikka. That was his favourite pastime. He had three sons who were all married. Once, his eldest son, Ganesh, went to his wife's relatives' house to attend a wedding. He was given a warm welcome and treated with special attention. Ganesh was very pleased by the hospitality shown to him. His wife's sister who was a mischievous girl, prepared a pikka for him filling it with salt and tobacco. As soon as Ganesh lit the pikka and blew out the smoke, something strange happened. The salt caught fire and crackled. Sparks flew in all directions. The people gathered there watched with both amazement and fear. But Ganesh was not scared. He continued to blow the smoke and then blew so hard that the sparks flew up into the sky higher and higher and got stuck there. They never returned for they had become stars!

06 The Flying Elephant

It is said that in olden times elephants had four large wings and could fly, and God himself used to ride on one of them. All was well until the earth was created and man began to live on the earth. The elephants would make a lot of noise flying up and down. Finally, God decided to do something to stop this problem. So one day, God invited the elephants to a grand feast. The elephants ate and drank to their hearts content and then went off to sleep. While the elephants were asleep, God cut off their wings. He gave two wings to the peacock who had no tail in those days, and that is how the peacock got its tail. The remaining two wings were stuck to the plantain tree and that is how it got those big leaves.

The elephants were furious to discover that their wings had been chopped off. They ran away to the jungle and ever since have been scared of men.

07 The Rich Man's Vessels

A rich man in a village owned vessels of all sizes. The villagers would borrow his vessels whenever there was a function in their house.

One day, the rich man was puzzled to see that a villager had returned two vessels more than he had borrowed saying that his vessels had given birth to two little vessels. The rich man knew that it was impossible but kept quiet fearing to lose the two new extra vessels.

Next time, the rich man gladly gave his vessels to the villager when he came to borrow them. But the villager did not return the vessels for months and at last the rich man went to ask for them. "Oh! The vessels have died," answered the man coolly.

"What does that mean?" shouted the rich man.

"If vessels can give birth they can die too," said the smart villager.

08 The Shepherd, the Tiger and the Fox

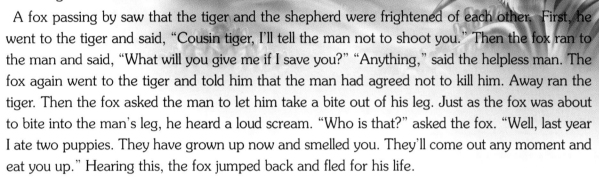

Once, a shepherd took out his sheep to graze in the field, when suddenly a tiger appeared. But the tiger was scared on seeing the shepherd's staff and thought it was a gun.

A fox passing by saw that the tiger and the shepherd were frightened of each other. First, he went to the tiger and said, "Cousin tiger, I'll tell the man not to shoot you." Then the fox ran to the man and said, "What will you give me if I save you?" "Anything," said the helpless man. The fox again went to the tiger and told him that the man had agreed not to kill him. Away ran the tiger. Then the fox asked the man to let him take a bite out of his leg. Just as the fox was about to bite into the man's leg, he heard a loud scream. "Who is that?" asked the fox. "Well, last year I ate two puppies. They have grown up now and smelled you. They'll come out any moment and eat you up." Hearing this, the fox jumped back and fled for his life.

09 The Dog and the Pig

Once a man had kept a dog and a pig to help him. But all that the animals did was eat and sleep. One day, the man ordered them to go and work in the fields. The pig obeyed his master's order and worked hard all day, digging the soil with his snout. But the lazy dog sat under a tree in the fields and slept all day. In the evening, the tired pig dragged himself home, while the dog raced to the field and rubbed out the pig's footprints. The dog then went home and told his master, "Master, I've really worked hard the whole day while this lazy pig slept." The pig protested but when their master saw the dog's footprints all over the field, he believed what the dog had said. The man scolded the pig for lying and being lazy and threw him out of his house. Ever since, the dog has remained man's friend while the pig has had to live outside the house.

10 The Tale of Echo

Hera, queen of Olympus was so annoyed with her servant Echo's talkative nature that she cast a magical spell on Echo under which Echo could only repeat what others said. This made Echo feel very lonely as she could no longer share her feelings with others and could not even express her feelings to handsome Narcissus, whom she loved. One day, Echo saw Narcissus admiring himself in a clear pool of water. The vain Narcissus admired his reflection and said, "I love you." Echo repeated the same words and meant it. But Narcissus thought that his reflection had spoken so and overwhelmed with pride, continued to stare at his reflection till he fell into the pond and got drowned. Echo was heartbroken and died. But she left her memory behind in the form of her voice. That is what we hear as echo when we go to certain hollow places.

11 The Girl Who Taught the World to Weave

When humans first began to walk on earth, they did not wear clothes because they did not know how to weave cloth. One day, God Matai decided to teach the art of weaving to a girl called Hambrumai. Sometimes, the girl sat by the riverside with her cloth and wove the ripples formed in the water; sometimes she spent the day in the forest and wove the designs made by the branches, or the patterns formed by the clouds above. When she wore the cloth she had woven, she looked beautiful, as if nature had gifted her all its gifts.

One day, Hairum, the porcupine, sneaked into Hambrumai's cave to steal the pretty cloth. As he tried to enter the cave, he pushed a rock that went rolling down to the riverside and, alas! crushed Hambrumai. The loom she used to weave her cloth also broke and parts of it flowed into the river. During its journey, the river carried those parts to various places. Wherever people found them, they learnt to weave. And the designs made by the girl became butterflies.

12 The Donkey Who Did Not Help

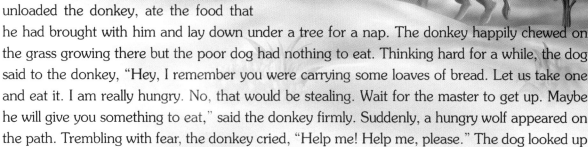

On a hot sunny day, a man was walking along a hilly path to the market. His dog and donkey was closely following him. At noon, the master unloaded the donkey, ate the food that he had brought with him and lay down under a tree for a nap. The donkey happily chewed on the grass growing there but the poor dog had nothing to eat. Thinking hard for a while, the dog said to the donkey, "Hey, I remember you were carrying some loaves of bread. Let us take one and eat it. I am really hungry. No, that would be stealing. Wait for the master to get up. Maybe he will give you something to eat," said the donkey firmly. Suddenly, a hungry wolf appeared on the path. Trembling with fear, the donkey cried, "Help me! Help me, please." The dog looked up where it was lying down and said, "I am feeling so weak that I do not have the strength to get up. Let the master awake and help you."

13 The Jester and the Stranger's Language

In the court of Maharaja Krishna Chandra of Bengal there was a very witty jester called Gopal. Once there was a new visitor in the court who could speak several languages.

But no one knew which part of the country he came from and what his mother tongue was. He would say, "I belong to this country. I speak the language of this land." The king asked Gopal to find out the man's mother tongue. That evening, when the man had gone to the market, Gopal entered his house and hid his lamps, lanterns and matches and waited for him to return. Finding his house in darkness, the man was puzzled. He hunted for the lamps and matches and said in Oriya, "I had left the house lighted. Wonder where my lamps have vanished?" Gopal ran out and told the king about his discovery. "The language that comes to a person's lips naturally is his mother tongue," explained Gopal. Later, the man accepted that his language was indeed Oriya. The king was highly pleased and gifted ten gold coins to his jester.

14 The Discovery of Fire

In the days before fire was invented, Cat and Bear were to get married. A fine feast was held but nothing was cooked. The animals grumbled because they did not want to eat the raw meat. Tiger, being the strongest animal, went straight to Firefly who had collected all the fire in the world and was sitting on it. But Firefly refused to give the fire to Tiger. Angry, Tiger got hold of Firefly. He was just about to crush her in his jaws when Firefly pleaded for her life agreeing to Tiger's demand. 'Take a dry leaf and let a drop of blood fall on it, then you'll get fire." Tiger did as advised by Firefly. The meat was cooked in the fire and the animals had a good time. A man who had secretly watched the tiger produce fire told the other men about it and since then men have been using fire to cook.

15 The Two Queens

Once upon a time, a king had two queens. The elder queen was ugly and wicked while the younger queen was beautiful and kind. Jealous of the younger queen, the elder queen decided to play a trick on her. She offered to comb the younger queen's hair and pressed a tiny gold pin on her head. Immediately the younger queen turned into a parrot. The king was heartbroken when his young queen went missing. Every day, the parrot would come and sit on the palace window and screech as if in agony. One day, the king caught the parrot and removed the golden pin from its head. And lo! The parrot turned into the young beautiful queen again. The king was overjoyed to have his dear queen back and banished the wicked queen.

16 The Bloody Knife

Hundreds of years ago, two warriors of the Micmac tribe got into a big argument. Soon, the quarrel erupted into a physical clash and knives were pulled out. Suddenly, one of the men slipped and fell into the muddy river close by. His blood stained knife slipped and went down to the bottom of the sea where it landed on a rock. The

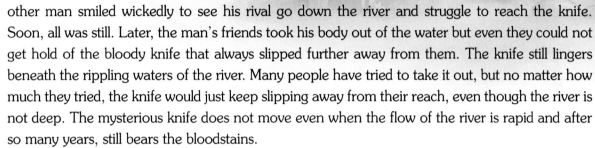

other man smiled wickedly to see his rival go down the river and struggle to reach the knife. Soon, all was still. Later, the man's friends took his body out of the water but even they could not get hold of the bloody knife that always slipped further away from them. The knife still lingers beneath the rippling waters of the river. Many people have tried to take it out, but no matter how much they tried, the knife would just keep slipping away from their reach, even though the river is not deep. The mysterious knife does not move even when the flow of the river is rapid and after so many years, still bears the bloodstains.

17 How Monkeys Got their Red Bottoms

Once upon a time, a group of eight boys and girls lived in a village called Dancing. Every night, they would light a fire and dance around it merrily. One evening, a monkey, dressed in a smart suit and hat, came to that spot. Then he began to play melodious music on his guitar and won the maidens' hearts. Seeing the monkey's popularity, the boys began to feel jealous of him. One night, the boys observed the monkey closely and discovered that he was a monkey after all! They planned to play a trick on him. They burnt some wood around the stone on which the monkey sat. When the monkey sat on the stone as usual, he jumped up and shrieked in pain. The hot stone had burnt his bottoms. That is how monkeys got their red bottoms.

18 The Monkey and the Mermaid

Hanuman was a monkey king and a very close companion of Lord Rama. When Ravana kidnapped Rama's wife, Rama asked Hanuman to rescue her. "Let's construct a bridge across the ocean. That way we can reach Ravana's kingdom," Hanuman commanded his monkey army. One by one, the monkeys started lifting heavy boulders and placed them on the sea. But to their amazement, they realised that as they turned their back to bring more boulders, the ones they had placed on the sea vanished! "Whose mischief is this?" shouted Hanuman angrily. He ordered the monkeys to dive with him into the sea. After swimming for a while, they noticed a few mermaids swimming in the water holding huge stones. "We have found the thieves!" screamed one of the monkeys. Slowly, the monkeys surrounded the mermaids. Hanuman came from behind and grabbed the leader of the mermaids, Sovann Macha. While she tried to free herself from Hanuman, they realised they had fallen in love with each other! Very soon, Sovann Macha told her mermaids to help the monkeys to build the bridge!

19 The Wise Judgement

Many centuries ago, a raft carrying three men reached the shore of Ceylon (now Sri Lanka). They were then taken to the king who learnt that one was a thief, the second was a wizard and the third was a mischief-maker who loved to play pranks on others and were banished from their kingdom. The king heard their stories and ordered that one thousand pieces of silver each be given to the thief and the wizard while the mischief-maker was imprisoned. Later, the king explained to his astonished courtiers, "Remember, the thief steals because he does not have enough. The wizard is wicked and unhappy because he too is jealous of what others have. So, if they have enough to live on, they won't trouble others. But the mischief-maker will always remain a mischief-maker." The courtiers praised their king's wisdom.

20 Two Fish and a Frog

Two fish called Multiwit and Centiwit lived in a lake with a frog called Uniwit. One evening as the friends were sitting by the lakeside, two fisherman passed by planning to come fishing to the lake the next morning. Hearing the fishermen's talk, the frog advised that they should leave the lake immediately. Hearing this Multiwit and Centiwit laughed. "Don't be frightened Uniwit. My many wits say that nothing will happen to us. We'll be safe and sound," spoke Multiwit. Centiwit, too, seemed unaffected and repeated the same words as Multiwit. "But my one wit says that I should flee from here," said the frog and left the lake that night. The next morning the fishermen caught the two fish in their nets, along with other fish. Hearing that his friends had been caught, the frog said in a serious tone, "It's better to follow one wit than be confused by too many wits."

21 Rearing a Colt

King Krishnadevaraya distributed eight colts to a group of chosen people, including Tenalirama, to take care of them. Tenalirama kept the animal in a closed room and fed it every day through a small opening in the wall. After three months, the King was pleased to see that the colts had grown fat and healthy. But he was surprised to see Tenalirama come without his colt. Tenali said, "My colt is so wild that no one dares to go near him. Please send a brave soldier with me to fetch him."

A long bearded soldier went with Tenali to fetch the colt. But, as soon as he peered through the hole, the hungry colt mistook his beard for grass and grabbed it. Finally, the wall was broken down to release the soldier. On seeing the colt, the king sternly asked Tenali why it was so thin and weak. "Your highness, when your strongest soldier was unable to manage a weak colt, you can imagine how difficult it would have been if it was strong." Tenali's intelligent reply astonished as well as silenced everyone.

22 The Boy and the Magic Brush

Once upon a time, there lived a poor orphan boy in a village. Often, he would pick up a twig and draw pictures of mountains, rivers and people. One day, a fairy gifted him a golden paintbrush.

The boy was overjoyed, and to his great wonder, whatever he painted with the brush appeared in front of him. Whenever he was hungry, he would paint a plate with food and all the things appeared on the plate. Soon, the boy became famous as 'The Boy with the Magic Brush.' One day, he was brought to the king's court. The king and his ministers went with the boy to the fields. "Can you create an ocean here?" asked the king. The boy painted the ocean and right then, the whole area was filled with water. The king then told the boy to make a boat, which the boy did. But the king was still not satisfied and ordered the boy to create a strong storm. Finally, the storm blew so violently that the boat overturned in the ocean killing the king and his ministers.

23 Pleasant Truth

Lakshmi was the goddess of wealth. Jyeshthadevi was the goddess of poverty. Once they were arguing about who was more beautiful. Just then, a merchant passed by and asked them what the matter was. The merchant was astounded to know who they were. Having listened to them, the merchant was asked to settle the matter. The merchant was in a state of confusion. He did not want to displease either of the goddesses. It was clear to him that Lakshmi was more beautiful, but how could he say that to Jyeshthadevi? She might become furious and turn him into a poor man.

So the clever merchant replied, "Oh Lakshmi, no one can be more beautiful than you when you enter someone's life, but Jyeshthadevi, you look the most charming and graceful when you leave." The answer pleased both the goddesses as both considered themselves winners. But it was the merchant's cleverness and wit that made him the real winner. Goddess Lakshmi blessed him with more wealth and Jyeshthadevi did him no harm either!

24 The Foolish Thief

On a full moon night, a foolish thief sneaked into a villager's house from the kitchen window. He spread out a cloth on the moonlit floor and entered the storeroom. The owner of the house was awake and had seen the thief. He quietly picked up the cloth that the thief had spread to collect the goodies. The thief on the other hand was unaware that the owner had seen him and taken away his cloth. He continued to place the stolen things on the cloth, thinking that it was still there. When the thief tried to locate the ends of the cloth to tie it, he was terribly confused to find his cloth missing. "I think someone has seen me," though the thief to raced out of the open window from where he had entered. But the owner was waiting for him there with a stick and gave him a good thrashing. Finally, the thief was allowed to go. He neither got the goodies nor his cloth that he used to cover his upper body.

25 The Buffalo

When God created the Earth, both men and animals lived together. God sent down a genie to Earth that brought plenty of food grains for the men and various grasses for the animals. One day, God handed the genie two identical packets, containing seeds of grains and wild grasses and commanded to sow the grains seeds first on Earth. But the absent-minded genie mixed up the two packets and first scattered the wild grass seeds on the soil. Soon, those seeds grew into wild grass and covered a huge area while the food grains got only a little space to grow. The animals had plenty to eat, but the poor humans were left hungry. When God heard the men grumble, he was furious with the genie and turned him into a buffalo. "From now on, you shall feed only on grass and help men in farming," said God sternly. That is why the buffalo does not have an upper set of teeth fit to eat grains.

73

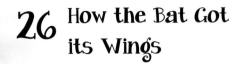

26 How the Bat Got its Wings

Long back, the bat was a little creature that did not have any wings. One day, God decided to arrange a game for two teams—animals without wings and birds with wingst. The little creature went to the animals and said, "May I join your team?" The animals laughed at the tiny creature and said, "You cannot play with us." So he went to the birds and asked them if he could play with them. "How will you play without wings? But we can help you," said the birds. The birds looked around and saw the top of a drum that belonged to the tribals. They took off the skin of the drum and made wings. Putting them on the bat, they showed him how to fly. In the beginning, the bat found it difficult to fly and would often fall down. Not losing hope, he would come to the birds every day and learn to fly. And one day to his great thrill, he was flying along with the birds.

27 The Story of Big Ears

A long, long time ago when the world was new, humans had big ears, so big that they would flap in the wind and go up and down. Man put these big ears into good use. Let us see how! He used one ear as a mattress and lay down upon it and the other ear he used as a blanket to cover himself with. But these long ears did not last for too long. God went out hunting one day. His eyes fell on the human who was sleeping soundly. "That looks like a new animal," said God and aimed his arrow at him. When he went close to the human, he realised what a fatal mistake he had made. "Oh! I mistook these big ears for an animal," God thought with sadness and guilt. But God quickly made up for his fault. He cut off the human's big ears and brought him back to life. God was happy to see a new man with small ears. So, that is the story of the small ears of humans.

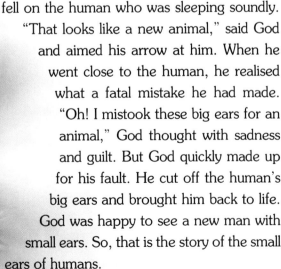

28 Whatever Happens, Happens for the Best

Once an old man's son went to a distant land to study. The villagers pitied his loneliness but he would smile and say, "Whatever happens, happens for the best." When the old man's son returned, the villagers were overjoyed and came to congratulate him. One day, his son fell off a horse and fractured his leg. Yet , the old man believed that it had happened for the best. Soon a war broke out and the king recruited all the young men of the village, except the old man's son. The king lost the battle and all his army men died in the battlefield. But his broken leg saved the old man's son.

29 The Key to Heaven

Once a fraud sage came to Tenalirama's village. He fooled the people with his so called miracles. Tenalirama heard about the sage and went to meet him. He heard the sage reciting mantras and to his surprise, discovered that the sage was repeating the same mantra and was actually cheating the people. Knowing that he was not a real sage as he claimed to be, Tenalirama suddenly plucked a beard from the sage's chin and shouted out holding the beard in the air, "Look, I've the key to heaven. This beard will open the doors of heaven for me." The others rushed to pounce on the sage and pluck a strand from his beard. The sage fled for his life and never returned.

30 War Drum

A hungry jackal was once wandering in the forest in search of food. Suddenly, he heard a strange noise—wooosh-dum-dum-shhhhh-dum-da-dum-da- dum! and started running out of fear. Quite exhausted, the fox decided to go and see where the noise was coming from. He laughed at himself when he saw the branches of a tree swaying in the wind and hitting the drum. Suddenly, he saw some food lying near the drum and ate to his heart's content.

Contents

The Story of the Month: The Maid of the Mist

The Story of the Month

The Maid of the Mist

01 The Maid of the Mist

Once upon a time in the charming countryside of America, there lived a young and beautiful maid. Her eyes used to glitter like dewdrops and her laugh was like soft murmur of a cascading stream. But at a very tender age she forgot to laugh. She lost her husband and knew no way to find her way through this immeasurable sorrow.

One day, she set out on a canoe, singing a song all to herself. Suddenly, her canoe was caught up in the rough waves and plunged towards the great falls. As the canoe flung up, the maid soon found herself in the gentle arms of Heno, the god of thunder, who lived in the falls. He carried her to his home safe beneath the thundering veil of water. Here the maid got a new life. In the warm company of Heno and his sons, her heart healed and she found a new urge to live. One of Heno's sons fell in love with her. Soon, they got happily married and had a beautiful son. But there was a shadow of grief in happiness. The maiden missed her people in her village a lot and longed to meet them. Her chance came in an unexpected way. Now, there came a large snake down the mighty river to where Heno was staying with his family. It planned to poison the waters of a village, which was incidentally the maiden's village. The people would drink the water and die. Then the snake would return and devour them until all were gone. When it was divulging this plan to its fellow companion, Heno overheard this. He immediately informed her about the imminent dangers of her people. She begged to him to let her return and warn them. "O kind Heno, please! let me go. I will warn them and I promise to return within an hour or so." Heno agreed. He himself raised her up over the falls and set her down so that she could warn her people. She met her villagers, told them about the danger that was looming large over their heads. She advised them to move up to a higher place until the danger was past. They agreed and vacated their place.

Later on, when the snake came to the village, it found not a single person dead. He realised that its plan had failed. Enraged at this unexpected turn of events it hissed and swore to search for them. Heno heard its voice and rose over the mist of the waterfall. He hurled a thunderbolt at it and killed it then and there. But it created a terrible chaos. The giant body of the snake flowed downstream and stuck just above the waterfall. It created a large splash and a lot of water just thrust down at the place, which was home to Heno and his family. Stunned by this horrifying turn of events, Heno did his best to stop this deluge, but it was in vain. Realising that their home would soon be destroyed. Heno along with his family members swept through the water of the falls and up in the sky. There they made their new home. Since then they live there and watch over the people of the earth. Heno continues to thunder as he used to do over the falls. To this day, an echo of Heno's voice can be heard in the thunder of the mighty waters of the Niagara Falls.

02 The Goblin and the Clever Farmer

One day, a farmer saw a goblin standing on his fertile piece of land. Thinking it to be a lucky charm he asked the goblin if he had buried treasures somewhere in the field. The wicked goblin replied, "Yes precious jewels which your eyes have never seen perhaps." The farmer said, "Since you have hidden it in my field, I should get a share of it too." The goblin said he would agree if the farmer gave him half his harvest for two years. "What is on top is mine while that which is at the roots is yours," confirmed the goblin. The farmer at once understood that the goblin was actually tempted by the abundant grain crop that grew on his land and agreed to the deal. For the next two years the clever farmer grew only potatoes, which is the root of the potato plant. So for two years, he took the root while the gnome had to take its leaves. The farmer won and took all the treasures.

03 Why the Fish Has Scales

Once upon a time there lived a farmer and his wife. They had a beautiful baby girl. She was the apple of their eyes and they loved her very much. She knew it and regarded the world to be at her feet. She was so much in love with herself that she would often go to the clear stream and admire her reflection on the clear water. One day, the king of the crabs spotted her at the side of the stream and wanted to befriend her. "Hello fair maiden! I am the king of the crabs. Would you like to be my friend?" But she sneered at him. "Have you seen your reflection in the water? I don't want an ugly crab like you to be my friend." Feeling insulted he decided to teach this vain girl a lesson. He jumped on her face and scratched it. And alas! All those scratches hardened to form scales. Moreover, she turned into a fish. Even today, you will often see scaly fish in clear stream quickly jerk away seeing their own reflections. Actually, they cry for their lost beauty.

04 Why Wisdom is Everywhere

Once upon a time there lived a spider named Anansi. He received a pot of wisdom from Nyame, the sky god who instructed him to share this wisdom among all the creatures of the world. But Anansi was unwilling to share it with anybody and decided to hide the pot on top of a tall tree. But it was difficult for him to climb up the tree with the pot tied around his waist in the front. Anansi's son was amused to see his father struggling and advised, "Father," he cried, "why don't you put the pot behind and then climb!" Anansi did that and found it very easy to climb up the tree. He realised that though he had the wisdom pot he lacked common sense, which his son had. Being angry with himself he threw the pot down. It broke into pieces and all the wisdom got scattered. Hence, no one in this world has all the wisdom in the world.

05 The Root of the Matter

In a village in Africa, there once lived a dog and a porcupine. One day, the porcupine was very hungry and asked the dog for food. The dog showed him a sugarcane field that belonged to a judge to feed on the sugarcanes leaving the roots. The porcupine liked the sugarcane very much and forgetting all about what the dog said, ate up the roots too. When the judge saw his field, he accused the dog for this. But the dog told the truth about the porcupine who flatly denied it and planned out with the judge to settle the matter in winter. Then one wintry morning both of them appeared before the judge. The dog was shivering in the cold and the porcupine quipped. "Your honour! See he is shivering out of fear. I think that settles the matter." The poor dog couldn't say anything in his defence as his teeth were chattering with cold. Taking his silence as an admission of truth, the judge pronounced him guilty.

06   Akbar Meets Birbal

Once emperor Akbar lost his way while returning from a hunting spree with his courtiers. Just then, they saw a man coming towards them and the emperor asked, "Tell me, which road goes to Agra?" The man looked at them curiously and a mischievous smile appeared at the corner of his lips. Sir! How can a road go? It cannot move," he chuckled. There was pin-drop silence. The courtiers staggered seeing a common man talking to the emperor like that! The man continued innocently. "Don't we travel on roads, sir?" Akbar stared straight down at him and suddenly, he began to laugh. "What's your name, young man?" asked Emperor Akbar. "I am Mahesh Das," the man replied. "Who are you, sir?" Akbar pulled off an emerald ring from his finger and gave it to him saying, "I'm emperor Akbar and I need witty, fearless people like you in my court. Come to meet me and now show me the road to Agra." Mahesh gladly showed him the way.

07   How Birbal Got His Name

Mahesh Das, went to meet Emperor Akbar one morning. When he reached the palace gates, Mahesh went up to the guards and said that he had come to meet the emperor. The palace guards looked at him and mocked, "Oh, really! The emperor has invited a rustic like you?" When Mahesh showed the ring Emperor Akbar had given him, the guards allowed but on condition that he share whatever gifts he got from the emperor. The emperor greeted Mahesh with open arms. "I am glad you have come, Mahesh Das. Ask for anything you desire. "O gracious king! I wish to be whipped fifty times", he answered. "I will keep twenty- five with myself and rest I will give to the sentries outside who asked for the share of gifts I get from you." Akbar understood everything and punished the sentries. Mahesh got a place in the court and was given the title Raja Birbal. Henceforth, Mahesh came to be known as Birbal.

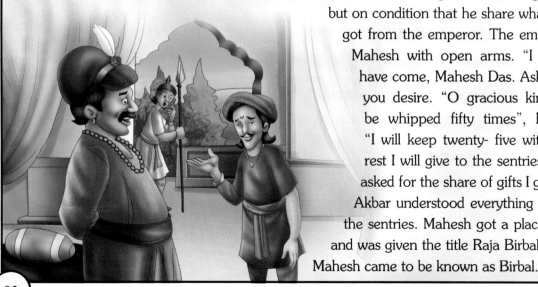

08 Jizo and the Old Man

Once upon a time there lived an old couple in Japan. New Year was just around the corner, so the woman said, "Take the flaxen textiles I have woven to the market so that we can get money to celebrate." It was a rainy day and it was very cold. On the way the man found Roku-Jizo, the six guardian deities of the children soaked with water. "Oh! They must be feeling very cold. Let me give these textiles to wrap them up in." Though he had to give up the idea of celebration, he was very pleased from within. At night, when the whole village was sleeping, suddenly the old man heard a noise. Some one was saying, "Let's put these things here. Tomorrow morning they will be very glad to find them." After a while, the old couple got up from their bed. They found a bag full of beautiful gifts and red clothes for the children of the locality. "It must be from Jizo-sama. I gave them wrappers and they have left these gifts for us," exclaimed the old man." And the whole village had a lovely New Year celebration.

09 Why Monkeys Mean Trouble

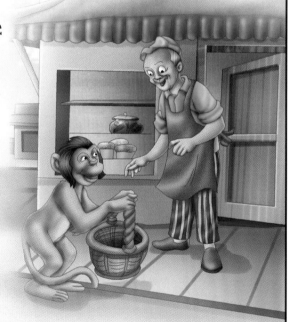

Once there lived an old couple. The wife was very good at making sweets. The man would sell them at his shop and earned a good living. One day while carrying her sweets to the shop, the woman tripped over a rock and fell. All the sweets got scattered over the ground. The woman began wailing, "See what trouble I bought!" Meanwhile, a monkey tasted one of the sweets and loved it. He went to the market carrying the woman's broken basket to buy some 'trouble'. Incidentally, he went to the old man. The man recognised the basket and asked him from where he had got it. The monkey narrated the whole story and said haughtily, "You old man! Give me 'trouble' if you can."

The old man grinned. He went in and came with a huge bag. Taking it he hurried away. After going a distance, he opened the bag to have his favourite 'troubles'. But alas! As he opened it out came two giant dogs growling. With a giant leap, he barely reached the lowest branch of the nearest tree. Since then, the monkeys keep to trees. But at times, they also try to create trouble for the humans.

10 The Red Peacock

King Krishnadevaraya was very fond of queer things. One day, a courtier gave him a red peacock. The king was impressed and rewarded him with twenty-five thousand gold coins. Now, this peacock was not naturally red. The courtier had it painted by a skillful painter and fooled the king. But Tenalirama smelled something was wrong in it and employed his informers to find all the good painters of the town. One of them confessed having painted a peacock red. Tenalirama asked him to colour four more peacocks red. Next day he went to the court with them. The king was pleased and wanted to reward him. "But my lord! Neither of us deserve any gold coins. The person, who actually deserves any reward, is this painter. He has painted these peacocks so well that they look like naturally red. Your deception is the proof of his talent," said Tenalirama. The king was impressed and rewarded him handsomely. The deceiver got his deserved punishment.

11 Silence is Golden

One day, a student went up to his teacher with a question that was bothering him for quite a few days. "Sir, is there anything good about talking a lot?" he asked. "I see so many people who talk so much. But my mother scolds me for talking a lot. She says only fools talk meaninglessly." His teacher smiled at him and said, "Toads and frogs croak day and night. But do we pay any attention to them? On the other hand, think of a cock. It only crows early in the morning. Look how much importance we give to the crowing of a cock. It starts our day. Now, I think you have got your answer. You decide what you would like to be, a cock or a toad?" "Yes sir", beamed the young lad. "I have understood. Talking a lot is of no use. It is important to say the right thing at the right time. He went back happily and learned to talk sensibly.

12 A Big Quiet House

Once there lived a man who was very unhappy with his home. He wanted his house to be larger and quieter. One day, he went to a wise woman to solve his problem. The woman assured him that he would have a large and quiet room soon. "Just do what I say. Your problem will be solved. Take a chicken, a horse, a cow and some sheep and put them into your house and stay with them." The man found this advice to be a little queer but did what she said. But quite contrary to his expected result, the house seemed a lot more small and noisy. He felt irritated and went again to the woman. "I did what you said but I have not got my desired result." "Don't lose patience, my dear. Just go home and put those animals back to their barn and then see the result," said the woman. The man did that. When he returned to his house, the whole house seemed so large and quiet. He then understood what the woman meant.

13 Crow Brings Daylight

A long time back, it was always dark in the land of Inuit until a wise crow set out for the east to bring daylight. After flying for many days, he saw a glow of sunlight across the sky. Suddenly, he noticed the daughter of the chief of the village taking her bath. He turned himself into a speck of dust and drifted down onto her fur coat. With her, he reached her home. There he floated into the ear of her little child and started crying. "Why are you crying, my dear," the chief asked. "Tell him you want to play with daylight balls outside," whispered the crow. The child did so. Her mother took out a daylight ball and gave it to him to play. As soon as the boy came out, the crow turned back to his self, took the daylight ball and headed towards his place. After he reached, his people he dropped the ball only to shatter it to tiny pieces. Light entered every home. But since the crow could bring only one ball, it is dark for one half of the year while it is light in the other half.

14 Tailless Dassie

A Long time ago, it was only the lion who had a tail. Being the king of the forest, the lion felt that all his subjects should also have tails. So he made tails for all the animals in his kingdom–each one was to have a unique piece. He summoned all the animals to his palace to hand over their specially tailored tails. All the animals went except one dassie, who was too lazy to go and requested the monkey to get his tail from the lion. The monkey thus took the dassie's tail from the lion. The dassie's tail was a small furry one and though the monkey got a nice long tail, he felt that a little furry at the end would look much better. So he attached the dassie's tail with him. The lazy dassie thus remained tailless till today.

15 The Court Jester and Hilsa Fish

The rains had just arrived in Bengal. Maharaja Krishna Chandra was disgusted because everyone around him was talking of fish. His court jester, Gopal came to his rescue and promised to stop this. The king in turn promised him a handsome reward. Next day, a fat woman with long hairy arms dressed in a bright red sari with her face covered, came to the court. Everybody broke out in whispers. The king asked her, "Who are you and what do you want?" But the woman kept quiet and did not utter utter a word. Angry at her silence, the king dismissed the court for the day.

"Maharaja, why are you angry? I just kept my promise." The voice was of Gopal's. He uncovered his face and said with a smile, "The court did not talk about fish today, not even once. So where is my reward?"

16 Force of Action

One day, a man found an old magic book in his attic. He went through it and found a paragraph where it was written that there was a pebble on the shore of the Black Sea, which could turn everything to gold. 'It is easy to identify the pebble since,' the book said, 'it is warm unlike other pebbles. The man went to the shore to search for the pebble. Every day and night he would pick up pebbles and feel them and to ensure that he did not pick the same pebble repeatedly he would throw them away to the sea. The days stretched to weeks and then into months. Even a year passed. But the man could not find the pebble. But he was not willing to give up. Then one day, while searching his lucky moment came. He picked up a pebble and it felt warm. What did he do then? Quite unfortunately, out of force of habit he flung it deep into the sea.

17 The Tortoise and the Eagle

Once upon a time an eagle used to visit a tortoise's place regularly to have the food that was being served to him. But he was selfish and never took the tortoise to his house. One day, a frog gave the tortoise a plan to teach him a lesson. The next day, the tortoise hid himself inside a gourd, given to the eagle to take it to his home and reached his home. "I thought you would love this change. I really look forward to dine with you," said the tortoise. The eagle was very angry to see him. He tried to attack the tortoise. But the tortoise clamped on the eagle's feet. The tortoise said, "First take me back to my home. Then only I shall free you." The eagle had no choice but to take him back. Before entering his house the latter said, "Friendship depends on the contribution of both the people. But you abused my hospitality. You are not invited to my house from now." Saying this he entered his house leaving the eagle to brood.

18 The Harpist and the Princess

Once there lived an orphan boy named Thi Hah in Burma. He was brilliant at playing the harp. One day, a jealous magician harpist put him under an evil spell and made him ugly with sores all over his body. He could only be his old self again if he married a princess. In despair, Thi Hah left his village and went to a forest. One day, while he was playing his harp, a princess heard him and wanted to take lessons from him. Thi Hah, covered in robes, started teaching her. After a while, when she was confident about her skill she declared that she would marry the person who would beat her at playing the harp. Many suitors came but the princess outwitted them all. Suddenly one morning, a mesmerising note filled the air. The princess walked towards the music and found out that it was her teacher who was playing this enchanting music. She kissed his gloved hand and to her surprise there was sitting a smiling Thi Hah. Thus, the princess broke the evil charm and they happily got married.

19 How Elephants Got Their Trunks

A long time ago, elephants used to have small beautiful noses. They were very proud of their nose and would always turn it up whenever they passed by any animal. One day, to teach them a lesson, the monkey sneaked into the house of a holy hermit and gathered some magic pepper. He mixed it with the lake water. When the elephants came to drink water from the lake, they all started sneezing. And much to their horror, each time they sneezed their noses became longer and longer. Meanwhile, the hermit from whom the monkey had stolen the pepper came out hearing all this noise. He understood at once what had actually happened. He rebuked the monkey for his deed and consoled the elephants saying, "Don't be sad. You now have another limb which is as strong as tree trunks. From now on your long noses would be called trunks." Quite happy, the elephants lifted their trunks in celebration.

20 Why the Opossum Has a Bare Tail

A long time ago, Long ago, an opossum was very fond of a raccoon's tail. "How beautiful its tail looks with rings all around it," the opossum often thought. He was determined to have a tail like that. One day he went up to the raccoon and asked him, "How did you get these beautiful rings around your tail?" Now the raccoon was quite mischievous. He wanted to play a trick on the opossum. He stroked his tail fondly and said, "Oh it was nothing! I just wrapped some portions of my tail with bark. Then I stuck it into the fire. The fur between the strips of bark turned black and the portions underneath the bark remained white." The opossum thanked him and scurried back to gather some barks. He too wrapped his tail with barks, built a big fire, and stuck his tail into it. But contrary to what raccoon said he got his tail burnt. The opossum screamed in pain. Since it was badly burnt, the fur never grew back. Since then, opossums have a bare tail.

21 Modesty Pays

Once there lived a driver in Qi, a state in China. One day, he drove past the place where he lived with his family with the prime minister sitting on his chariot. Excited to see him, his neighbours and his wife cheered his name. But he drove past all of them with an arrogant air about him.

In the evening, after returning from his work, his wife told him how arrogantly he behaved while the prime minister sat modestly in the chariot. The man understood his mistake and learnt to become modest. The prime minister too noticed the change in his attitude and asked the reason behind this. The man replied, "My attitude was always so wrong. Now, I have realised it." The prime minister appreciated him and recommended his name to the king for an official post in the court.

22 The Ridge Forest

A long time back there lived a hunter. One day while he was waiting, he saw a bear coming from the mountainside. As he quickly took his aim, he saw the bear walking along a narrow ledge on the side of the mountains. He thought, "If I shoot it now, it will fall into the deep gorge. That will be of no use to me." So he waited.

Suddenly, he saw a small bear coming from other side of the ledge. The ledge was so narrow that it was impossible for both the bears to cross at the same time. The hunter kept watching. He was expecting a fight between the bears. But surprisingly, the big bear sat down and allowed the small one to climb on his back and cross over. The hunter was overwhelmed to see this. He realised how human beings lack compassion, cooperation and fellow feeling which he saw in these two bears. Since then, he stopped hunting and devoted all his time to understand animals. The forest came to be known as 'The Ridge Forest.'

23 King Maon and the Willow

When Maon, the king of Ireland was a child, his uncle Cavoc usurped the throne killing his father and exiled young Maon to Gaul, which is modern day France. Years later, Maon attacked Ireland and defeated Cavoc. Maon however, did not want to reveal his true identity and called himself Maon, the Mariner Another thing that he tried to hide were his long ears. To keep this a well-guarded secret forever a barber was chosen to give him a special haircut. After the haircut, the barber was killed. Once, Maon spared the life of a young barber who promised never to reveal anything. The boy however said everything to a magic willow tree. Unfortunately, the willow was used by Maon's court musician to make a new harp. The next day, when he first touched its strings at Maon's court it said, "Two horse's ears have the Mariner who speaks." Maon felt very ashamed and no more did barbers have to lose their lives.

24 Tenalirama, the Messenger

Tenalirama was the favourite courtier of King Krishnadevaraya. This made some courtiers jealous and planning to ruin Tenalirama's reputation, they convinced the king that Tenalirama was actually a spy of the neighbouring state. The king banished Tenalirama who reached the neighbouring state with a heavy heart and tried to bring peace between the two states. He went to the king and told him that King Krishnadevaraya wanted to a friendly relation with him. Hearing him, the king said in a surprised tone, "But we have heard that he is planning an attack on us." At this, Tenali very wittily said that they too had heard the same about this neighbouring state and advised him to send gifts and a peace message to their king saying, "Our king understands that war never serves any good." Meanwhile, in Vijaynagar, the king learnt about his ministers' foul play. When he received those gifts he praised Tenali's sagacity and welcomed him back.

25 The Boy and the Wolf

One day, a boy was looking at a thick jungle from his rooftop. He had heard so many scary stories about the jungle that he never dared to enter it. But he had a hidden desire in his heart to brave a wild animal.

It was daytime. The forest looked less menacing. The boy saw a wolf passing by his house. From the rooftop, the wolf did not look very fierce. The boy felt like scaring this animal away. He knew he was at a safe distance. He screamed, "Hey you ugly creature! How dare you to come near my house. Get off right away or I will set my dogs on you." "I was just passing by," replied the wolf in soft tone knowing that he was in the enemy territory. "Just passing by! Huh! Is this a thoroughfare? Get lost, I say!" The boy was stunned at his own courage. But then the wolf said, "It is very easy to be brave from a safe distance." And he growled so loud that the boy ran inside the house.

26 The Lady in White

Every day young Bethushka used to take her flock of sheep to graze near a grove of birches. She always had a spindle in her pocket, which her mother gave for spinning. But she was more fond of dancing around the birches in her little steps.

One day, while she was dancing, a lady appeared. She had a long golden hair and was dressed in a white flowing silk. "Will you dance with me? I can show you some nice new steps," she said. "Oh I would love to. But my mother will scold me if I don't spin," replied Bethushka. "Oh don't worry about that. I will help you," the lady assured her.

The next day, Bethushka danced with her like never before. At the sundown when it was time to go home, Bethushka found that the spool was filled with fine thread. But her mother suspected something. Bethushka told her everything. "Why dear, that was the White Lady of the Birch Grove!" she exclaimed. And when she opened the pouch given by the white lady, to their astonishment, they found birch leaves of gold.

27 The Farmer and the King

Once a farmer grew a huge watermelon, the biggest ever to be grown. He thought of giving it to the king as a present. At that time the king was touring the land in disguise. Incidentally, he came to the farmer's place and saw the watermelon. "How much does this cost?" asked the king fascinated with the watermelon. "I am not selling it to you or to anybody. I am going to present it to the king," replied the farmer. "I see," said the king. But what if he refuses?" "Then he may go to the devil," snapped the farmer. A few days later, the farmer reached the king's court. He at once recognized him but did not reveal it. "Your Majesty! I have this watermelon for you. I have grown it myself," said he. "Oh! This is marvelous! But I am sorry I can't take this," replied the king. The farmer could see that the king was having a little fun with him. "Then, Your Majesty," said the farmer in a mock timid tone, "you already know my answer."

28 The Horse's Revenge

A long time ago, there was drought on Earth and the horse and the buffalo had a fight over food. The horse was badly injured and after recovery, decided to seek revenge on the buffalo. He coaxed a man into helping him. The man rode the horse and beat the buffalo everytime they pased by. One day, the man captured both the buffalo and the horse and tied them to a tree. Quite surprised at the man's behaviour, the horse asked why he had been tied up. The man laughed and said, "Dear friend, you have been of so much help. You have told me about the buffalo's milk and also taught me how to ride horses. I need both of you to help me always." The horse felt shattered and realised that he was punished for betraying his friend, the buffalo. Since then he decided never ever to betray anyone, not even the captors.

29 Transformation

Once, a frog impressed by the cuckoo's melodious voice, requested the cuckoo to teach him to sing. The cuckoo agreed and tried to teach the frog to sing. But all that the frog could do was croak in his harsh voice. "Croakkkk…" shouted out the frog as the cuckoo tried to teach him the basic notes of music. Making the frog sing was so difficult for the cuckoo that he started dreaming about the frog's hoarse voice and actually picked it up. One day, while practicing, the cuckoo found out that he could no longer sing melodiously and the harder he tried to do so, he could just produce a harsh cawing sound. This was how crows came into being.

30 The Singing Fir Tree

One evening, when the church bells chimed, a woodcutter heard a strange melodious music. At first, he ignored it as a figment of his imagination. But next day, when the same thing happened the woodcutter set out to find its source and he came near a hundred year old giant fir tree. To his amazement, he found that the song was coming from its trunk. The woodcarver instantly wished to carve on its magnificent bark. The fir tree was felled and the woodcutter carved a beautiful statue of Virgin Mary out of it. Then it was placed on the alter of the church. Suddenly, the statue of Mother Mary opened her mouth and once again sang those sweet melodious notes for the last time.

31 Birbal, the Child

One day, Birbal arrived very late at the court. The emperor was very displeased. "My child was crying. And I had to calm him down." Birbal explained. "It seems you know nothing about rearing a child. I'll teach you that. Now, you act as a child and I'll be like your father." "I want a cow", demanded Birbal imitating a child. A cow was brought in. "I want its milk…" wailed he. The cow was milked and a glass of it was offered to Birbal. He took a sip and started crying, "I don't like it. Put it back into the cow. Put it back. Put it back…." The emperor did not know what to say. He decided to go ahead with the court's proceedings.

Contents

The Story of the Month: The Fortune Seekers

The Story of the Month

The Fortune Seekers

01 The Fortune Seekers

In a village lived four scholars, who were good friends. Exhausting all their wealth in acquiring knowledge, they decided to leave their village and seek a fortune elsewhere. Before leaving, they went to the wise woman of the village who was known to have magical powers.

As soon as the four scholars entered her house, the wise woman sang aloud:

Mere knowledge has value less

Double it with intelligence or you'll mess

The four scholars shared with her their desire to seek a fortune in another land as the people in their village hardly valued them.

"Ok, I'll give each of you a feather. Secure it properly to your waist and wherever the feather falls, it means the owner will find his fortune in that land," said the wise woman and handed each of them a white feather. The four scholars travelled for days and one morning, one of the feathers fell down from one of the scholars' waist. They found a copper mine there and the first scholar said, "This seems to be my fortune. I'll wait here for you all while you go ahead and seek yours." "Do you call this a fortune?" said the other three scholars and decided to proceed on their journey. After travelling for some days, one evening, the second scholar's feather fell down. Here they found a silver mine. "Aha! I've found my fortune too," exclaimed the second scholar. "But this is no good a fortune at all," said the other two scholars and decided to go ahead till their feathers fell.

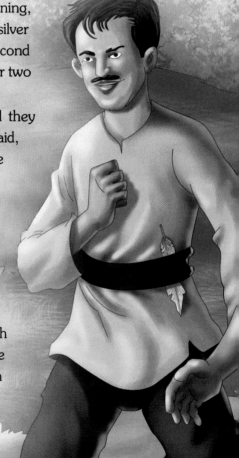

The second scholar decided to wait for them there till they returned. As the two scholars proceeded, one of them said, "Friend, will we get a good fortune so that we can drive away our poverty?"

"Sure we will. We are so learned and besides, the wise woman has guided us. Don't worry and continue your journey," said the other. Feeling quite excited, the two scholars went further towards the North.

One day, as they were walking, the third scholar's feather fell. They looked around the place and found a gold mine, "Wow! This is really good," exclaimed the fourth scholar. "Yes! I'll take this as my fortune," chuckled the third scholar. The fourth scholar decided to continue on his journey alone till his feather fell down. "All right friend, go and seek your fortune. I'll wait for you here," said the third scholar as his friend took leave and ventured further north. Having travelled for some time, the fourth scholar came to a snow clad plateau. There he saw a man groaning in pain and bleeding profusely. He was moved by the sight he saw. A toothed iron discus was moving around the man's head and cutting into his skull. The scholar went up to the man and said, "Who has done this to you? Can I help you in any way?" As soon as the scholar said these words, the toothed iron discus flew off the man's head and settled around the scholar's head. The scholar moaned in pain as the other man smiled and said, "Now you'll suffer as I had till another man with a feather comes and rescues you."

Meanwhile, the other three scholars had come out in search of their friend. They met the man whom the scholar had freed and came to know about their friend's plight. But they were helpless. They decided that they did not want the same fate to befall them and so returned to their respective mines and fortunes.

02 The Frog and the Mouse

Once upon a time there lived a frog and a mouse who were very good friends. The frog lived in the water of a pond and the mouse lived in a small hole beside the pond. Every day, the frog would hop to the land and meet his mouse friend near. One day, the frog decided to play a prank on the little mouse. Next day, when the mouse was busy talking about his day's adventures, the frog tied his own foot and the mouse's foot together with a string. And so when it was time to go home, the frog hopped back to his pond taking the mouse with him. "Help! Help!" The mouse screeched but the frog didn't care. He was having a hearty laugh. The helpless mouse didn't survive in the water and dies. After a while, a hawk saw the mouse' body and swooped down and picked it up. Alas! The frog was still tied to the mouse and couldn't escape. The hawk took them both away and the frog met his end as well.

03 Clever Anansi

Anansi a spider, Sana a tiger and a goat were friends and lived in the same house. Sana's kids were also with them. Intending to have the house to himself, the tiger growled angrily one day, "Leave the house at once and let me live in peace." So Anansi and Sana decided to go away. As they left, the tiger ran behind them. Running quite fast for some time, they came across a stream. Anansi made Sana and her kids stand still and said, "Abbra Kadabbra!" And lo, they turned into white pebbles which were carried away by the water to the other side of the stream. On reaching the shore, Sana and her kids turned into goats again. "Wow! That was so exciting," rejoiced Sana's kids. They all hid behind the bushes while the tiger came near the stream. "I'll eat you, Anansi," the tiger grinned wickedly. Anansi at once weaved a silver thread and threaded across to the other side of the stream. The tiger failed to catch any of them and returned home.

04 A Question of Numbers!

Tenalirama was a very clever courtier in Krishnadevrai's court. One day, intending to outwit Tenalirama's cleverness, Krishnadevaraya asked him, "Tenalirama, can you tell me how many bangles your wife wears on her hands?" Tenalirama thought for a moment and replied, "Pardon me, Your Highness, I don't know." At this Krishnadevaraya smiled and said tauntingly, "How can that be, Tenalirama? You see her hands every day while she serves you food, still you don't know how many bangles she wears? I can't believe this!" To change the topic of discussion, Tenalirama suggested they go to the garden. Quite happy that he had managed to outwit Tenalirama at last, Krishnadevaraya agreed. They walked down a flight of stairs and came into the garden. As Krishnadevaraya strolled on, Tenalirama asked, "My Lord, you climb up and down these stairs every day, can you tell me how many steps there are?" Krishnadevaraya was embarrassed because he actually did not know how many steps there were. He smiled sheepishly and changed the topic, thus accepting his defeat graciously. Tenalirama had got the better of him once more!

05 For Horned Animals Only

Once the elephant threw a party for the horned animals. The hare who lived nearby was tempted to attend, so he stuck a pair of antelope's horns made of wax on his head and went to the party uninvited. No one recognised him and complimented him for such beautiful horns. The hare drank and danced with the other animals and dozed off to sleep. In the morning, he woke and found his horns missing as the wax had melted. Fearing the elephant, the hare escaped but the elephant and the deer saw him. All the animals started chasing him. The hare hid in a cave. The elephant was the first to reach the cave, but could not enter inside with his huge size. He peered in and with his long trunk started to pull hard at a tuft of grass, which he mistakenly believed was the hare's tail. The other animals too joined him while the hare pretended to be agony and shouted. The grass finally got uprooted and all the animals fell back, on top of each other while the clever hare managed to escape.

06 Wild Goose Chase

Two hunters were once passing through a lonely forest. Suddenly, one of them saw a fat, wild goose on the branch of a tree. "Look! What a wonderful hunt," he exclaimed, with delight. Immediately he took out his bow and arrow and aimed it at the goose saying, "This goose will make a delicious stew." Hearing him, the other hunter said, "Stew! What rubbish! It will make a good roast." Both the hunters then started arguing whether it should be roasted or stewed. As their fight became fiercer, they went to the head of their clan with the dispute. On hearing both their pleas, the head of the clan said, "All right, divide the hunt into two equal halves. Roast half of the wild goose and stew the other half. Then each of you will be satisfied." Happy with the head's decision, the two hunters went back to the tree where the goose had been sitting. But alas! In their argument they had lost their hunt, for the goose had flown away!

07 Struck by Lightning

Chengez, a rich man and his valet was riding along a forest. Chengez rode very fast and his valet was left far behind. This annoyed Chengez and he shouted, "You lousy, keep pace with me." With great difficulty, the valet reached Chengez, who hit him hard on his head for being slow. The valet was very upset at being ill treated. Suddenly, the sky became dark and it started thundering. Chengez was scared of thunder and hid his face in his horse's mane. The valet saw this to be an opportunity to teach Chengez a lesson. Each time it thundered, the valet hit Chengez hard on the head. Chengez thought that lightning had struck him. Being hit the tenth time, Chengez fell off his horse and became unconscious. The valet too feigned unconsciousness. When Chengez regained his senses, he saw his valet lying on the ground beside him. He shook him up saying, "I fainted after being struck so many times, you fainted at one go." The poor valet hung his head, without saying a word. Chengez then realised what had actually happened. He realised his mistake and never ever ill treated his valet.

08   The Lion and the Hare

A lion once caught a hare. As he was about to eat it, the hare said, "Oh king of beasts, I'm too small to satisfy your hunger. Let's go and hunt something bigger in the village." The lion agreed and off they went together to the village. The lion caught a healthy bull and the hare managed to catch a lean and thin donkey. Wanting to teach the lion a lesson the hare cleverly managed to convince the lion that his donkey was healthier than the lion's bull saying, "My lord, a fat animal always gives out steam when struck. Strike the donkey and see for yourself." The donkey, who was covered in dust, let off a cloud of dust and a pitiful howl when the lion struck him. Amazed, the silly lion agreed to take the donkey and leave the bull for the hare. He also agreed to give the hare his spacious den and go and live in a far, far corner of the jungle.

09   The King's Cats

Krishnadevrai's kingdom was once overrun by rats. They became such a menace that the King got some pedigreed cats and distributed them among the people. To feed these precious cats, he gave each family a cow. Tenalirama too received a cat and a cow. My children need this milk more than this fancy cat does," he thought and with some idea in mind, he fed the cat a plateful of hot milk. The cat burnt its palate and refused to drink any milk after that. However, it attacked all the rats in Tenalirama's house and soon his house was rid of the rodents. Tenali, meanwhile, fed his wife and children with the milk. His neighbours were quite upset. Their cats did not even look at the rats and were quite content with the milk they were fed. They spied on Tenalirama and realised that he was feeding his family the milk that was actually meant for the pedigreed cat. When the king came to know this, he summoned Tenalirama and asked why was he not feeding his cat with milk. Tenalirama then explained to the king why his cat had fed on the mice in his house while the other cats were so well fed with milk that they never bothered to look at the mice. The King understood his mistake and ordered the people to stop feeding their cats milk.

10 Birbal is Brief

Once Akbar called his courtiers and asked them to tell him the difference between truth and falsehood. Everyone tried to reply but their answers failed to impress the king. Birbal stood quietly in a corner. Akbar noticed this and went up to Birbal and asked, "What happened Birbal, don't you have a reply to my answer?" Birbal smiled and said, "The answer is four fingers, Your Majesty." Akbar looked perplexed and stared at Birbal, trying to understand the meaning of his words. Birbal understood Akbar's dilemma and continued, "Your Majesty, the difference between truth and falsehood is just four fingers because what you see with your eyes is the truth and what you hear may not be true and so it could be false. Hmm… but what do you mean by four fingers?" enquired Akbar. Birbal smiled and said, "You see with your eyes and hear with your ears and the distance between ones ears and eyes is just four fingers! " Akbar was quite amused and said, "You are indeed very clever." Birbal bowed his head in respect and walked away.

11 The First Swim

A baby polar bear lived with his mother by the cold Arctic Ocean. He was very unhappy because he could not swim. His mother had tried her best to teach him, but failed as he refused to get into the water and clung to his mother's warm furry back saying, "Noooo… I fear getting wet." All the other polar bears used to make fun of him. One day, Mother Bear returned home and found Baby Bear crying bitterly. She ran to him and asked, "What's the matter, Son? Why are you in tears?" "Booo…hooo I'm the laughing stock of all my friends because I can't swim," sobbed Baby Bear. Suddenly, Mother Bear noticed that Baby Bear was sitting in a puddle of water and his fur was all wet with tears. She immediately asked, "Aren't you feeling uncomfortable now? You're wet." Baby Bear realised that there was nothing to fear about getting wet and went happily into the sea with his mother. As he swam on his back with his paws up, Mother Bear looked on at him with pride.

12 Tenalirama's Escape from Exile

Once King Krishnadevaraya was very displeased with Tenalirama and banished him from his kingdom. Tenalirama obeyed the king's orders and started on his journey. No one knew where Tenalirama went. After a few days, Krishnadevaraya was passing through the forest on his horse. Suddenly his eyes fell on Tenalirama, who was climbing up a tree. The King's anger had not yet subsided and realising that Tenalirama was still in his kingdom, he flew into a rage.

"How dare you disobey my orders! Why are you still in my kingdom?" the king demanded angrily. "Pardon me Your Highness. I have travelled the whole world but wherever I went, I found that it was a part of your kingdom. So, now I'm climbing this tree and trying to go into the other world," Tenalirama replied humbly. Hearing Tenalirama, the king burst out laughing and pardoned him. Tenalirama happily went back to Krishnadevaraya's court.

13 The Clever Wife

Gundoba, a very pious and generous brahmin, used to go to the Vaijnath temple and feed the poor which irritated his wife. One day, when Gundoba went to the Vaijnath temple as usual, he met a poor brahmin and invited him for a meal. While Gundoba finished his prayers, the brahmin went to Gundoba's house. When Gundoba's wife saw the poor brahmin at the door, she was livid and decided to chase him away. She invited the brahmin inside with tears in her eyes and said, "My husband invites brahmins and then ties them to a post and thrashes them up with a grain pounder. But I'm helpless…" The brahmin at once turned around and left.

When Gundoba returned and came to know that his guest had left because he was not given a rope and the grain pounder, he ran after him shouting, "I've got the rope and the pounder for you. Please stop." But the poor Brahmin fled for his life and Gundoba returned home sadly.

14 The Two frogs

Once upon a time in Japan, two frogs–one from the town of Osaka and the other from the city of Kyoto decided to go and see the world beyond their homes. So, they planned to meet halfway between the two towns. A high mountain separated the two towns. The frogs climbed the peak from different sides. "If only we could see both the towns from here, we can decide where we want to live," said the frog from Osaka. Hearing this, the frog from Kyoto suggested, "If we can stand on our hind legs and hold each other tight so that we don't fall, we can actually see our destination." So the two frogs stood up with their nose facing the direction of their destination. But the foolish frogs forgot that when they stood up their eyes were behind their heads and although they thought that they were seeing their destinations they were actually looking at their hometown. So to them, Osaka and Kyoto looked like a copy of each other. The foolish frogs dropped their idea to know the world and went back to their respective hometowns.

15 The Green Children

One day in the land of the green-skinned people, where the sunlight never reached and there was a strange twilight-like light, two children, one boy and one girl noticed a mysterious cavern while passing through a jungle. Curious as they were, the children decided to explore the cavern. As soon as they stepped into it, they heard some soft chimes of bells coming from a distance. The children were so enchanted by the sound that they started moving towards its direction till they came to the other side of the cavern which opened to the world of humans.

When the children stepped into their newfound land, they were blinded by the strong sunlight and soon fell unconscious. A little later, some villagers discovered them near the cavern and carried them to their village. For the first few days, the children only ate beans and nothing else. Unfortunately, the change in the climate took a toll on the boy and he died. But the villagers were able to bring the girl back to her health. Since then she stayed with the villagers and by and by lost her green colour.

16 The Reader of Minds

When Emperor Akbar built his new palace at Fatehpur Sikri, he gave a bungalow to Birbal near his palace. This made the other courtiers jealous and they decided to spoil Birbal's reputation. So, in Birbal's absence they falsely praised Birbal before Akbar saying he could read people's minds. Deciding to test Birbal's mind-reading skill, Akbar summoned Birbal to his court and asked, "Wise Birbal, I've heard that you can even read people's mind now. Can you tell me what I'm thinking now?" Birbal understood that it was a conspiracy and said, "Jahanpanah, I cannot read a great mind like yours, but I can tell you what the others are thinking." He then loudly proclaimed that the courtiers were thinking about Akbar's welfare. The courtiers couldn't help but admit that Birbal was right. Akbar understood the entire drama that had enfolded before his eyes. He realised that Birbal was truly a wise man.

17 Dreams

One evening, an elephant was wandering in the jungle when he stumbled upon a gathering of demons. Seeing him, the demon king cried excitedly, "Oh! This is the same elephant I was eating in my dreams last night. Let me eat him up to make my dream true." The elephant was so frightened that he lost all his power of resistance and stood there helplessly as the demon king started advancing towards him. Just then his friend, an owl came there screeching excitedly, "I have found her! I have found her!" The owl then declared that he had married the demoness in his dream last night. So he had come to make his dream true by marrying the demoness. "I'll never marry an owl," shouted the demoness. The demon king realised what the owl meant and allowed the elephant to go saying dreams are never true. The elephant thanked his friend and hobbled away with him.

18 The Broken Promise

A prince and a goatherd were good friends. The prince promised to make his friend a royal guest once he became the king. But when he became king, he forgot all about his promise and his friend, the goatherd.

One morning, the king got up in great pain as he had been pricked by needles all over his body. Doctors and magicians from all over failed to cure him and he continued to suffer. One day, while the queen was bathing in the river, an imposter stole all her royal clothes and jewellery. Wearing the royal finery, the imposter claimed to be the queen and took the real queen in rags to the palace as a maid. While washing clothes one day, the queen fainted by the riverside. The goatherd found her and came to know the truth. They hurried to the palace and with his magic, the goatherd removed all the needles in the king's body. The prince opened his eyes and saw his friend. "Forgive me, my friend," said the king and embraced the goatherd. He banished the imposter, made the goatherd his chief advisor and lived happily with his queen.

19 The Lazy Brahmin

Khusi, a lazy brahmin once got a big pot of flour from a rich man. He took the pot home and hung it from his bedpost. "Aha! I've got so much flour. Indeed I can make money if I sell it," thought the lazy brahmin and started dreaming.

He dreamt of how he would sell the flour in exchange for thirty rupees, with which he would buy two goats, then two cows and became a dairyman. And then he would open up a sweet shop and his sweets would sell like hot cakes. He would earn so much money that he would ultimately become a famous gold merchant. He would buy a bungalow, have a beautiful wife and be the proud father of two smart but mischievous children. When his neighbours would complain about them he would hit them with a stick. "Better behave, kids!" shouted the brahmin in his dream and hit the pot. Bang….. Crash…… broke the pot and all the flour was spilled on the ground, leaving Khusi with his empty dreams.

20 The Tiger's Whisker

A lady once went to a wise hermit seeking help to win over her
husband's love who she felt had become cold and aloof after returning
from the war. The hermit agreed to help her with his magic
potion but asked the lady to fetch a tiger's whisker to
make the potion. The lady agreed and started visiting
a tiger in the forest. Initially, the tiger used to snarl
at her, but as it got familiar, it became friendly and
allowed her to come near it. One day, as the lady
was caressing the tiger, she pulled a whisker off
its face and ran to the hermit. The hermit took the
whisker and threw it into the fire. "What have you
done?" shouted the lady in amazement. The hermit
smiled and said, "Look! Win over your husband's
love the way you've won over the tiger's." The lady
understood what the hermit meant and went home happily in the knowledge.

21 How a Rumour Takes Wing

A brahmin once had a strange feeling in his mouth and spat out a heron's feather. Quite
confused, the brahmin returned home and told his wife about it, asking her to keep it a secret.
But the brahmin's wife confided in her neighbour who interpreted that several feathers had
come out of the brahmin's mouth. She shared the secret
with the dhobi's wife who further confided in her
friend interpreting the feathers as herons. By
evening, the brahmin's tale was known to
the entire village but the final version
being that birds come out of the
brahmin's mouth. People flocked
to the brahmin's house to witness
the miracle inspite of him denying
to have performed any miracle. At
last the brahmin gave in and asking
the people to be seated, ran out
through the back door into the forest
and hid there for days till the people
realised that it was a rumour.

22 Who Bodes

Everyone in Krishnadevaraya's kingdom believed that Ramaiyya was jinxed and his presence boded ill. It was a common belief that if anyone saw Ramaiyya in the morning, he would not get a morsel of food the entire day. To test the belief, Krishnadevaraya invited Ramaiyya to stay with him for a day. That very day, Krishnadevaraya had to remain hungry the whole day as his food was ruined by a swarm of flies in the royal kitchen. Convinced that Ramaiyya was jinxed, Krishnadevrai ordered him to be beheaded.

On the day of his execution, Ramaiyya met Tenalirama on his way to the scaffold. Tenalirama whispered something in his ears and asked him to repeat the same before the king. As Ramaiyya was standing on the scaffold, the king arrived and asked Ramaiyya his last wish to which he replied, "The king is a greater jinx than me because I saw his face today and the result is that I'm going to lose my life." The king felt ashamed and sent Ramaiyya away with lots of gifts and wealth for his family.

23 The Monkeys Go Fasting

One day, all the monkeys of a forest decided to observe a fast. Before they started the fast, the chief said, "Let's collect the food with which we'll break the fast before we begin." The others agreed and went to look for food. They brought huge stacks of ripe bananas and placed them before the chief. The delicious smell of the bananas was very tempting. An old monkey suggested, "Let's peel off the bananas." "We should keep a banana each in our mouth before we begin the fast so that we don't waste time when we'll break the fast," suggested another. So the monkeys peeled off the bananas and kept a banana each in their and finally started the fast. They kept looking at each others face and soon swallowed the bananas and that was the end of their fast.

24 The Secret of the Casket

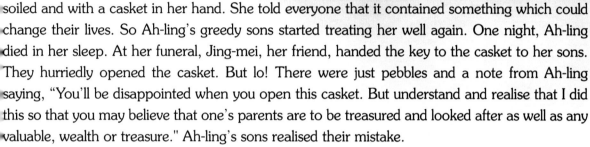

Old Ah-ling having distributed all her wealth among her four sons, decided to stay with each of them for three months every year. But soon Ah-ling felt unwelcome in her sons' houses. One day, while Ah-ling was in her eldest son's house, she went out in the morning without informing anyone and returned late, her clothes soiled and with a casket in her hand. She told everyone that it contained something which could change their lives. So Ah-ling's greedy sons started treating her well again. One night, Ah-ling died in her sleep. At her funeral, Jing-mei, her friend, handed the key to the casket to her sons. They hurriedly opened the casket. But lo! There were just pebbles and a note from Ah-ling saying, "You'll be disappointed when you open this casket. But understand and realise that I did this so that you may believe that one's parents are to be treasured and looked after as well as any valuable, wealth or treasure." Ah-ling's sons realised their mistake.

25 When Goddess Lakshmi Begged

King Prithvi was very proud of his wealth. One day, he bought some precious jewels and threw them into a ditch to flaunt his wealth. This annoyed Lakshmiji and she made Prithvi lose all his wealth and his kingdom in gambling. Out of despair, the king left his kingdom with his wife, Rohini and stayed on the outskirts of another kingdom.

One day, Rohini found a necklace in her courtyard near a dead snake. It belonged to the queen and she had declared a handsome reward for the one who could find her necklace. Rohini went with her husband and returned it to the queen. "Tell me what you want," asked the pleased queen. Rohini humbly said, "Grant me that on Diwali, no house in your kingdom, except mine is to be lighted." The queen agreed and on Diwali, Lakshmiji, finding darkness every where, had no choice but to go to Rohini's hut. "I won't let you in till you promise to return our fortune," said Rohini to the Goddess of Wealth. Lakshmiji agreed and blessed the couple.

26 The Hunter

Once upon a time there was a hunter called Hunter. One day, he spotted a deer in the wood and aimed an arrow at it. But suddenly, the deer turned into a man and introducing himself as Abdallah, asked Hunter if he would give up hunting if he had enough money to support his family. Surprised, Hunter asked from where would he get money if he gave up hunting. Hearing this, Abdallah gave him 50 gold coins and said, "Take this money, my friend and leave hunting. I know you are a kind man and you don't like to kill animals. Whenever you need money just come to this rock and say, "O brother Abdallah' and I'll come to meet you." Hunter went back home with a cheerful heart. Since then, Hunter and Abdallah became very close friends. Gradually Hunter became a rich man. He shared his riches with others and advised people not hunt animals.

27 The Lost Land of Wales

Many years ago, where the river Dyfi meets the Atlantic Ocean, a large kingdom of Cantrefy Gwaelod stood in the low-lying land. It was protected from the sea by a series of well-constructed dams. During the reign of Prince Gwyddno, the kingdom reached the pinnacle of glory. But as days passed the king and his subjects started leading a dissolute life whiling away the time in drinking and pleasure. Even the damkeeper forgot all about his important responsibilities. Only one man named Teithryn kept himself away from these senseless pleasures and kept warning fellow citizens about the impending danger of the kingdom being submerged by the sea water as the dams were decaying without care. Then one day, Teithryn's fear came true and the gigantic sea waves swallowed the entire kingdom.

28 The Treasure of Largo Law

A long time ago, a ghost lived in the area around Largo Law in Scotland, a place rumoured to have many hidden treasures. The ghost had decided to share this information with a brave shepherd and on condition that there should not be any sound of cock's crowing or horns blowing while they met, else there would be a disaster. The shepherd killed all the cocks within hearing distance and requested Tommie Norrie, the herder not to blow his horn in the morning which was the scheduled time to meet the ghost. But Tommie disobeyed and played the horn while the ghost was about to divulge his secret. The ghost immediately stopped hearing the horn and lo! Tommy Norrie fell down dead on the ground.

29 The Cock's Ruse

It was mid summer and the Sun was very strong. "Oh, this sweltering heat," complained the people and cursed the Sun. This made the Sun angry and he withdrew from the Earth, making it very cold and dark. Everybody pleaded with the Sun to return but he refused. At last the cock was sent to request the Sun but he too failed. The cock decided to return and requested the Sun to come to his rescue if he was attacked by the wild cat. The cock hid himself on the way and crowed loudly. The Sun came running out to look for the cock as he had promised him. So, from then on, whenever the cock crows, the Sun comes out, looking for him.

30 The Boastful Crow

A crow once challenged a swan to a flying competition. The young swan took up the challenge and they started off. The crow boastfully flew in circles performing many acrobatics in mid air. The swan followed him in silence till at last they flew over a wide stretch of water. By now, the crow was tired and found it difficult to balance himself. Caww... the crow pleaded for help. The kind swan took pity and saved the crow who promised never to be boastful again.

Contents

The Story of the Month: The Angry King

The Story of the Month

The Angry King

01 The Angry King

A long time ago, in a far away kingdom of tobacco growers, ruled a wise king called Hari Ka Buskid. In his reign, the people of his kingdom were very prosperous, for the king himself looked after the welfare of the people. He would go up to the farmers and give them tips on improving their tobacco plantations. His kingdom was famous for tobacco production and people from neighbouring kingdoms would come and barter their goods in exchange for the rich, golden tobacco. Just before the harvest festival, the king called his subjects and said, "I am going on a long voyage and will be away for quite some time. But do look after the fields. Work hard and continue to grow tobacco so that our kingdom remains famous forever for producing good tobacco." The people loved their king and regretted his absence at the Great Harvest Festival. The king too expressed his regret and left for his long voyage. "We'll miss our noble King," said a farmer. "That's true but we'll have to really work hard in the fields as the king has asked us to do," said the village chief. The people nodded and started preparations for the Great Harvest Festival. Finally, the day of the festival came. The young men danced and sang

> *Here we celebrate the grand day*
> *Remembering what our King always says*
> *Come let's dance and sing*
> *Till the church bells ring*

After the harvest festival, the people started working hard in their fields. They reaped a good harvest and made good profit. For almost ten years, the people of King Hari Ka Buskid's kingdom worked hard and produced rich, good tobacco. They made huge profits and everyone became rich. The kingdom became prosperous and the people started living in grand houses and wore rich clothes and jewellery. But the king was yet to return back. Slowly, the people forgot all about the king and his advice. They became proud and lazy. Most men started spending their time idly and neglected the fields. Soon, the kingdom lost its charm. The fields became barren and the people became poor. Their grand houses and rich clothes looked shabby. In almost all the houses, the women would complain, "There's no food in the house. We're going to starve." But the men would still not work. One day a severe earthquake came. The people ran out of their houses in fear towards the mountain. Suddenly, there was a thundering crack in the mountain and out came King Hari Ka Buskid. The people were wonderstruck to see their king. "Why have you stopped working in the fields and become poverty-stricken?" the king demanded angrily. The villagers shook in fear. "Now start reworking in your fields. Sweat your brow until you make these barren fields fertile again. I shall wait for the good harvest," said the king and smashed his fist into the mountain. A huge hole appeared where his fist struck and the king leapt into the hole and disappeared, leaving his subjects awe-struck.

It is believed that until today, King Hari Ka Buskid is waiting in the mountain. He smokes tobacco when he is in a good mood and the smoke reminds his subjects of his presence and his advice.

02 The Frog King

In a marshy swamp, there once lived a colony of frogs. The frogs led a happy carefree life, eating and playing the whole day. There was a group of young frogs in that colony that wanted a leader. "Let's choose a leader," suggested Henri, a smart young frog. "Let's go to God and ask for a leader," suggested a frog. Croak! Croak! The others agreed and they all went to God seeking a leader. Finding it quite amusing, God threw a huge log into the marsh as the frogs' leader. Plook! The log fell into the water with a loud sound, scaring the frogs. Henri boldly jumped onto the log and realised it was just a log. They again went to God asking for a new leader. This annoyed God and he sent Kiki, the stork. Kiki had been hungry for days and when she saw the marsh full of frogs, she started gobbling them one by one until she became so fat that she could hardly fly. The foolish frogs sobbed and regretted having asked for a leader.

03 The First Garlic

Once there was a beautiful maiden. Her mother took pride in her daughter's beauty and would often wish, "God, do give me a rich handsome suitor for my daughter." One day, a rich merchant saw the beautiful maiden and wanted to marry her. The mother willingly got her daughter engaged to the rich merchant. But an evil man killed her fiancé, hoping to marry her, who in turn was slain by the merchant's slave. Full of grief, the maiden decided to go up the sacred mountain and ask God to take her away so that her beauty would not take any more lives. But, alas! On her way, she was struck by lightening and died. One day, the mother saw some green shoots springing up from her daughter's grave. She pulled them up thinking it to be weeds and saw some white teeth-like structures. Suddenly, she heard a heavenly voice saying, "Don't throw them. These are your daughter's teeth." Thinking it to be God's grace, the mother sowed them everywhere and that is how we got garlic.

04 Moment of Madness

Once there was a man who was obsessed with gold. He had no greater love than pure solid gold bars. "The very sight of gold excites me," he would often say. One day, the man was passing by a jeweller's shop and saw the jeweller handling a bar of gold. "Wow! That looks great," he exclaimed with delight. He was so attracted by the sight of the gold bar that he walked into the jeweller's shop and snatching the gold bar, ran away. The jeweller raised a hue and cry saying, "Help! Help! I'm being robbed of my gold bar by this wicked man."
The policemen ran after the man and caught him. They took him to the court before the judge. On hearing how the man had stolen the gold bar, the judge asked, "Why did you steal the gold bar in front of so many people? Didn't you fear being caught?" The man smiled and said, "At that moment I saw only the gold bar and nothing else."

05 The Mango Charm

Bholu, an illiterate man, had the power to perform a miracle—he could load mango trees with ripe fruits. Whenever he performed the miracle, he would eat his share and distribute the rest among the poor villagers. One day, a youth named Keshav met Bholu and begged him to teach Keshav how to perform the miracle. After much pleading, Bholu agreed and said, "All right, I'll teach you. But remember not to misuse your power and never to lie, else the magic words will lose its power." Keshav agreed and Bholu taught him the magic words. Keshav happily went home and started using his magical power. He would utter it several times in a day and get baskets of mangoes, which he sold in the market and made good profit. Soon, Keshav became very rich. Seeing his prosperity, the king summoned Keshav and asked him the reason for his success. Keshav lied that he had learnt from the scriptures. The king then asked him to perform it. But alas! He lost his power as he had lied.

06 Cooking by Candle

Mullah Naseeruddin had a bet with his friends that he would be able to survive a night on a chilly mountain without anything to warm him up. Taking only a book and a candle, he sat there through the freezing night. Next morning, he claimed his winnings from his friends. "Are you sure you didn't have anything to warm you?" asked his friends. "No, nothing at all. I only took a book and a candle," replied Naseeruddin. "That explains everything. You are not supposed to take anything there. But you took the candle and that saw you through." They refused to give him any credit. A few days later, Naseeruddin invited those friends for dinner. Dinner time passed but they were not served anything. "What are you making, Naseeruddin? When shall we have our dinner? " asked his friends. "It will take a little more time. Come, I'll show you." In the kitchen, they saw a huge pot under which a candle was burning. "You remember the bet? See, I am heating this pot with this candle since morning. It is not warm enough yet. You'll have to wait for your dinner," he smiled at them amusedly.

07 The Troublesome Slippers

Abukashan had a pair of worn-out boots. One day, he lost them in a public bath and instead took home a pair of the judge's boots, mistaking them to be a gift from his friend. The judge then imposed a heavy fine on Abukashan. Holding the boots responsible for his trouble, Abukashan threw them out of the window. But they landed up in a fisherman's net and damaged it. So Abukashan decided to get rid of them by burying them. But while he was digging a hole, his neighbour saw him and reported to the police thinking he was hiding some hidden treasure. The judge told a tearful Abukashan, "You must realise that as good things come, they must go too at the right time."

08 Honeyguide's Revenge

Once there lived a greedy man named Gingile. One day, while hunting, he heard the call of a honeyguide, a little bird that helps humans to find beehives. He followed it and reached a big fig tree. The bird chirped, "It is here! It is here!" After driving the bees away by creating a small fire with dry twigs, he climbed up the tree and took out all the combs dripping with mouthwatering rich honey. But he did not give the honeyguide its share. Determined to teach Gingile a lesson, the little bird after a few weeks, guided Gingile to another tree. Not realising that it was the same bird, Gingile followed it and climbed up a tree as shown by the honeyguide. But, to his horror, Gingile found a leopard taking her mid-day nap. Scared, he jumped from the tree and broke several bones, whose scars stayed with him for the rest of his life.

09 The Fear of God

In a village, there were two brothers who were always up to some mischief. They always kept all the villagers, including their parents, on their toes. All of them were just fed up with their pranks. One day, their mother asked a priest to put the fear of God into them thinking that it might make them mend their ways. The priest called the younger one first to sit and have a talk with him. When he came, the priest asked, "Where is God? The boy gave no answer. "I am asking you where God is," he demanded. The boy remained silent. But when he was asked the question for the third time, he jumped up from his seat and ran straight to his elder brother almost breathless. "What's the matter?," his brother was curious. "We are in big trouble!" the younger one gasped. "Why? What happened?" asked the elder one warily. "God is missing," said the younger boy, "All of them think we have something to do with his absence!"

10 The Rabbit, the Elephant and the Whale

Once, a rabbit was taking his morning stroll when he bumped into an elephant. "Good morning!" he greeted the elephant. But the elephant just ignored him, for he was too small. The rabbit felt disappointed. He was passing by the sea when he spotted a mighty whale. He called out to him but here too he was insulted. Then the rabbit made a plan. He went up to both the animals separately and challenged them to a tug-of-war contest. After that, the rabbit gathered the strongest vine. The elephant tied one end of it around his huge waist. The rabbit took the other end and said, "When I shout 'pull,' pull with all your might." He then went to the whale and said the same thing. After a few seconds he shouted, "Pull!" Hearing this, both the animals went their way. But they were astonished to find that the vine refused to budge. Soon, it could not take any more strain and snapped into two pieces. The poor elephant tumbled down the steep valley and the whale dashed his head on a coral reef.

11 Bearded Fool

One day, an old man read a book where it was clearly written that men with long beards were fools. This disturbed him quite a lot since he too had a long beard. He had always felt very proud of it but now that the book had given such a piece of information, he felt it necessary to get rid of his beard. He gathered the beard in his hand and held the tip over the candle flame. Soon the tip caught fire and within seconds, the beard was all gone. But before he could understand anything, a spark went up into the hair on his head and it started burning. And to his horror within few moments his hair turned into ashes. He screamed aloud. His cry brought all the neighbours into his house. They were stunned to see a scorched face and the smoke curling up around it. "How did it happen?" they inquired, dowsing him with water. "Nothing," sighed he, "the book said men with long beard were fools and I proved it right."

12 Tenalirama's List of Fools

Once, a horse trader came from a far-off land to King Krishnadevaraya's court and took an advance of five thousand gold coins promising to give a horse of fine breed in two days. In the evening, the king found Tenalirama scribbling some names on a piece of paper. He said, "I am jotting down the names of some of the greatest fools on earth." The king was surprised to see his name at the top of the list. "What does this mean?" he demanded, "you consider me a fool?" "Any person who gives a stranger five thousand gold coins and expects him to return them must be a fool," replied Tenali. "Oh, you think he will not return. But what if he returns?" the king asked. "Nothing. I'll just scratch your name from the top and put his name instead," replied Tenalirama.

13 The Turtle and the Leopard

One day, a turtle went to visit a leopard. He met Mrs. Leopard and said he could ride Mr. Leopard as a horse. When Mr. Leopard came to know about the comment, he was furious. He went to the turtle's house and demanded an apology. Seeing the leopard angry, the turtle got scared and flatly denied to have said that. "Then let's have a talk in front of my wife and you deny it in front of her," said Mr. Leopard. The turtle then said that he would not be able to go since he was terribly ill. So, the leopard agreed to carry him on his back. Then the turtle tied a rope around the leopard's mouth so that he would not fall if he felt feverish. He also took a stick to keep away flies. When they reached home, Mrs. Leopard laughed to see that the turtle had done what he had said. Realising his mistake, the enraged leopard flogged the turtle hard, the marks of which are still there on his shell.

14 The Golden Tree

Once upon a time there lived a king who had four beautiful wives. He loved his youngest queen the most because of her generous nature. Being jealous, the other queens conspired against her and had her banished from the land. The banished queen then started living in a small cottage in the forest of a neighbouring kingdom. One night, the king dreamt about a golden tree under which he saw his dearest queen sitting and weeping. He at once realised that he had wronged his wife. Early next morning, he went out in search of the golden tree. He travelled for months and at last came to a lake with boiling water. There in the middle of the lake, stood the golden tree. Risking his life, he stepped into the steaming water and went near the golden tree. But there was no sign of his banished queen. Feeling very sad, the king wept and wept till his heart was cleansed of his sin. Then breaking a branch from the tree, he entered into the adjacent forest where his wife lived. Thus, at last the two loving hearts met again.

15 Dick Whittington and His Cat

A long time back, there lived a poor boy named Dick Whittington. He went to London to seek his fortune. There he got the job of a scullery boy in the house of a rich merchant. Dick had a little room of his own. He stayed there with his cat. One day, one of the ships of the merchant was leaving for a far-away land for trade. The merchant asked everyone to send something of their own that could be traded for gold. Dick had only his cat. He sent it. Everyone at the merchant's house, except the cook, loved Dick. He made Dick's life miserable. So one day Dick ran away. But on his way, he heard the Bow Bells chime, "Turn away Whittington, thrice the Mayor of London." Dick was surprised and turned back. On his return, he found that the merchant ship had returned and his cat had been sold for a good fortune to the King of Barbary, whose palace was full of mice. So Dick became a rich man and later on became the Mayor of London thrice.

16 Five Men in a Cart

Guru Gampar ordered his four disciples not to do anything without his permission. One day, while travelling in a bullock cart, Guru Gampar fell asleep and his turban slipped off. Since the guru had asked them never to do anything without his permission, none of the disciples got down to pick it up. "Next time anything falls, pick it up at once," Guruji growled after waking up. So, the next time the bullock dropped his dung, they picked it up. Guru Gampar was disgusted and made a list of things that should be picked up if they fell from the cart. Sometime later, the cart lurched violently. Guru Gampar just flew from the cart and fell into a ditch. He yelled at his disciples to pull him out. "Your name is not in the list, Guruji. We know you are testing us. We won't pull you out," said his obedient disciples. "Throw me the list and a pen, you fools!" screamed Guruji. They did so. The Guruji wrote his name on the list and threw it back to them. Only then did the disciples pulled their Guruji out of the ditch.

17 Meeku's Long Tail

Little Meeku Mouse was very unhappy as his school mates teased him for his extraordinary long tail. One day, at school, he found Chinu mouse sitting alone and crying. Though Chinu was one of those who teased Meeku, still he went up to Chinu and knowing that Chinu had dropped his purse in Tommy Tomcat's field, promised to help him. So after school, Meeku went to Tommy's field. Tommy was keeping a strict vigil but still Meeku managed to sneak into the field. He saw a purse in Tommy's hand.

Tommy Tomcat was looking for a place to hide the purse. He tied the purse with a thin root of a banyan tree and hid the purse along with the root in the bush. But poor Tommy! What actually happened was that he tied the purse with the tail of Meeku who was hiding there. At last, Meeku's tail came to use and since then no one teased him any more.

18 How Humans Got Eyes

When God created humans, he forgot to give them eyes. So human beings were always tumbling over each other and were unable to see the beautiful world around them. God felt sorry and came to Earth to amend his mistake. He sat under a fig tree to rest. On one of the tree's branches, a crow was eating plums. The seeds were falling on the ground. "Ah! I can make eyes with these seeds," thought God and made eyes with them. But he made no eyelids and lashes and so humans couldn't close their eyes. As such it was difficult to know they were asleep or awake. Once it happened that the Water Sisters came to visit a family of humans at night. They were very offended to find no one greeting them. But in the morning their misunderstanding was cleared. They promised to help the humans. They made lashes out of a peacock's delicate feather-ends and fixed them onto the eyes of their friends. Since then humans could shut and open their eyes.

19 The Coconut Daughter

Once upon a time, there was a land of coconuts which was ruled by an heirless king. One year, the coconut harvest was extraordinarily good and the king had a tank full of coconut oil. The king looked at the oil and wished for a child. Suddenly, he heard a voice. "Father! Please take me out. I am your daughter." The king was astonished to see a beautiful girl in the tank, which only a few moments back was filled with oil. He named the girl Nyaragi. The king made her a new house where there was no fireplace because he feared that since she was formed of oil she might get destroyed if she was too warm.

The winter arrived. Nyaragi felt cold. She wanted to warm herself. "A small fire won't hurt me," she thought. She slipped into the kitchen. As she felt comfortable, she kept inching closer to the fire. The next morning, when the king woke up, Nyaragi was never to be seen again.

20 The Sun-Goddess of Korea

Byun-soon, Dael-soon and Hae-soon were three sisters. They were very nice girls and God was very pleased with them. One day, as a tiger came out of the forest and attacked them, God rescued them and took them to Heaven. He turned Byun-soon into a bright twinkling star, Dael-soon into the moon and Hae-soon into the sun. But Hae-soon was very coy and when the people came out of their house to look at her as she appeared in the sky, her face glowed in embarrassment and became so bright that the people were almost blinded by her radiance. Extremely shy as she was, she found this suitable for her and continued to glow brightly since then.

21 The Bed Bug and the Mosquito

Once upon a time, there lived a bed bug with his family in the big beautiful bed of the king of the land. They had a good time living there drinking the king's sweet blood and sleeping in the cozy corners of the bed. One day a mosquito came into the room. He was delighted to see the soft plush bed. "Ah! The person sleeping here will definitely have soft skin. I can easily take one sip of his blood," he said in excitement. The bed bug heard this and came out. "How dare you intrude into my domain? I don't indulge any kind of trespassing," screamed he. "Please let me stay for one night. I will taste the king's blood once and go off," requested the mosquito. The bed bug relented. At night after the king had fallen asleep, the mosquito came out. His temptation was too much. He bit the king on his neck. This awakened the king. The angry king ordered his servants to find who had bitten him. Meanwhile, the mosquito had flown off. The servants upturned the bed mattress only to find the bug family and killed all of them.

22 Just One Question

One day a scholar from a faraway land came to the court of Emperor Akbar. He threw an open challenge to Birbal who was one of the courtiers of the emperor and revered as a very intelligent man. The scholar said, "I challenge you to answer 100 easy questions or one difficult question." Birbal accepted the challenge and settled for one difficult question. The scholar asked, "Tell me which came first into this world—the chicken or the egg?" "Chicken," replied Birbal confidently. "How do you know that?" asked the man, a note of triumph tracing his voice. "We had decided that you would ask me one question and you have already done that. So I won't answer any more questions of yours," stated Birbal. The scholar's jaw dropped at his defeat.

23 Magical Pumpkins

An old man once told his son on his death bed, "After I die, put some pumpkin seeds on my grave." Saying this, he breathed his last. The son fulfilled his father's last wish. The pumpkins grew. After a while, one of them was ripe enough to be harvested. When the son cut the ripe pumpkin, gold coins poured tinkling down onto the floor. As the other pumpkins became ripe, the son got more gold coins and became rich. Soon, the king of the land got to know about the young man's newfound wealth. The greedy king sent his soldiers to rob all the gold coins. But all the coins turned into snakes on reaching the king's palace. To seek revenge, the enraged king sent back those snakes in baskets to the son. But at the young man's place, the snakes turned again into jingling gold coins.

24 Tenali's Forecast

Once, at a grand feast given by the Commander-in-Chief of Vijaynagar in celebration of his son's birth, Tenalirama forecasted that the child would outshine his great father. Everyone was surprised at Tenalirama's prediction. Some jealous courtiers coaxed the king into verifying the truth of Tenali's statement by putting him into an intelligence test. Two identical golden pitchers, one hollow and other solid, were hung and Tenali was asked to identify them by observation only. Tenali looked at them minutely and heaved long sighs. He then identified the pitchers correctly! The king, though happy, was very surprised. Tenali explained, "The chain that the right pitcher was hanging from was taut due to the pitcher's weight whereas the left one was not. Moreover, when I sighed, the left chain moved a bit. And everything became crystal clear." He then went away with the two pitchers as a reward, leaving the other courtiers gaping.

25 The Foolish Fat Fox

A kind-hearted lion once kept a fox as an attendant. Every day, the lion used to kill an animal and ate it as much as he could. The fox ate the leftovers. One day, the lion gave him the chance to choose an animal to eat. When he chose a bison, the lion killed it and both had their food. Soon it became a routine. Gradually the fox became as fat as a barrel. Thinking himself to be as strong as the lion, the fox said to the lion, "From tomorrow why don't you choose an animal and I kill it?" The lion was shocked at his stupidity. He tried to make him understand that a fox would never be a lion. But nothing worked. The next morning the fox went to kill an elephant. But the elephant hit him with its trunk and crushed him under its feet. The lion thought "Arrogance made him blind" and tears rolled out of his eyes.

26 The Meditating Parrot

Once Maharaja Krishnadevrai of Vijaynagar received a beautiful parrot as a gift. The king called his personal valet and ordered him to take good care of it. "If something bad happens, I will have you beheaded right away," he warned. The valet was very careful about the parrot. One day, to his horror, he found the parrot dead. He rushed to Tenalirama knowing that only he could save his life. Hearing everything, Tenali ran to the king gasping, "Maharaja! Your parrot, your parrot…" "Yes, tell me, tell me, what has happened to it?" The king jumped up from his throne, tensed. "It seems it has gone into meditation. It neither moves nor speaks," replied Tenalirama. The king was surprised and went to see the parrot. He found the parrot dead. "Why did you lie to me?" the king demanded. "Maharaja," replied Tenali "hadn't I lied, you would have beheaded the valet then and there. How can one take the responsibility of one's life? Only the Almighty can do that." The king realised his mistake and thus the valet's life was saved.

27 War of Words

Once upon a time, a king sent a message to the ruler of a neighbouring country, "Send me one diamond as large as a pigeon's egg or else…" The king of the neighbouring land wrote back, "We don't have such a diamond and if we had…" The first king felt insulted and declared war on the other. The fighting went on for several months until a third king appeared in the scene as a peace maker. He arranged a meeting. It appeared that neither of the kings wanted war as one meant any other diamond while the other meant that he would have given the former the diamond if he had it. Both the kings realised that all fault lay with their unfinished statements and vowed to write their thoughts completely and clearly in the future.

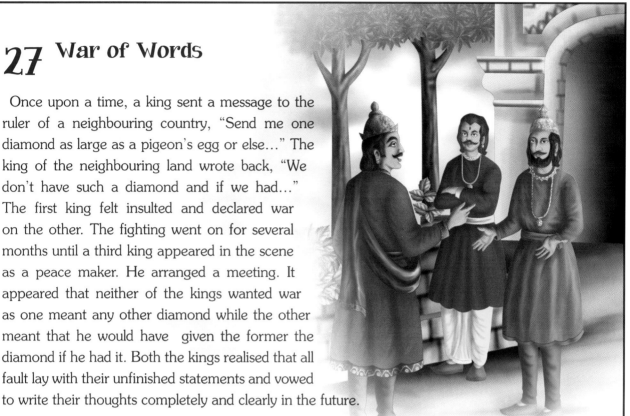

28 The Donkey and His Music

Once a donkey and a fox were good friends. One night, while roaming around, they reached a cucumber farm. The cucumbers looked very luscious and juicy and the donkey had his fill. The fox ate fowl from an adjacent farm and was all too happy. This continued for a few days. One particular night, the donkey was very cheerful and expressed his desire to sing. "That's fine. But don't sing now. Your song will wake everyone up and we will be in danger," advised the fox. But the donkey was adamant and said, "You know nothing about music. And you're jealous of my talent." Saying so, the donkey started singing, mistaking his hoarse voice to be melodious. The donkey's braying broke the watchman's sleep. He took a sturdy stick and ran towards the donkey. The fox fled while the foolish donkey got a good beating.

29 Coloured

Many many years ago, when the earth had just been created, an owl ran a business of his own. He had a dyeing shop that all the birds visited regularly. One day, a crow stepped inside the shop, his feathers elegantly styled and asked the owl to dye him in a colour that would set him apart. In those days, crows were white. The owl led the crow to the dyeing room and put him into a bucket of indigo. When he was taken out, the crow's feathers were straightened and he was glossy black. The crow was terribly furious. He was not in a mood to entertain the owl's logic. He shouted so loud that it cracked his voice forever and since then he could only say "Caw! Caw!"

30 Disputed Waters

Once, a man sold his well to a farmer. But when the farmer went to draw water from the well, the man stopped him from doing so. "I sold you only the well. I never mentioned water. So, if you want water from it then first you'll have to pay me separately." The farmer obviously refused to accept this and the case was taken to the court. After hearing everything, the judge turned towards the man and said, "Since you sold the well you don't have any right to keep water in it. Pay rent to the farmer for keeping water or else take it out of the well." The man realised that he had been outwitted and from then on created no more problem.

31 Treble Trouble

Once a man was caught stealing a bag of onions and was taken to the judge. The judge gave him a choice of three punishments: eat the onions he had stolen, bear hundred lashes or pay a fine. The man chose to eat the onions thinking, "Why should I bear the pain of a hundred lashes or pay a fine. Rather, eating the onions would be a good choice." Thus thinking himself to be very clever, the man started having the onions one by one. But after having a few, his eyes were burning and water streamed down from them. His mouth too felt as if it was on fire. "I can't eat anymore onions...", said the man blowing in air into his mouth. But after he had received a few, he could take no more and he screamed, "I can't bear it! I'll pay the fine." So he paid the fine. But he became the butt of jokes for others for having suffered three punishments for one crime.

Contents

The Story of the Month: The Baboon and the Tortoise

The Story of the Month

The Baboon and the Tortoise

01 The Baboon and the Tortoise

Once, a baboon and a tortoise became friends. They would steal figs from a farmer's trees. One day, the tortoise suggested to the baboon that they should plant their own fig trees before the farmer or his fierce dogs would catch them. The baboon agreed, but being a lazy animal, he did not care for his tree, which gradually dried up and died. The tortoise meanwhile tended to his tree carefully and as a result, juicy figs appeared on the tree. Since the tortoise could not climb up the tree to pluck the figs, he asked the baboon to pluck them for him. But the cunning baboon ate up all the ripe figs and said, "Tortoise, I've tasted all the figs. They are still unripe so I can't bring down anything for you." The baboon then laughed and ran off. The tortoise was very sad and decided to take revenge on the baboon. One day, the tortoise was standing next to a beehive, listening to the humming of the bees. When the baboon passed by and asked him what he was doing, the tortoise said, "Baboon, this music is very good but too soft. If you wish to hear it louder, then take this stick and beat it up and down this branch," The baboon was unaware of the bees and followed the tortoise's advice. At once, the humming grew louder, out came a swarm of bees and attacked the baboon, stinging him all over his body. Screaming in pain, the baboon immediately dragged himself to the river, the swarm racing and buzzing after him. Splash! The baboon dived into the river and found a little relief from his agony, but as soon as he popped his head out of the water, the angry bees stung him again and again. It was some time before the bees left the baboon and droned back to their nest. At once, the baboon jumped out of the water and was dismayed to see bumps all over his face and body. His pain grew as he tried to pull out the bees' stings and so he scratched and scratched himself and has been doing it ever since. In a fit of mad fury, the baboon swore to teach a lesson to the tortoise and raced as fast as he could. He was about to bite the tortoise who was gazing curiously at a hole in a hollow tree. "You villain," screamed the baboon. This will be the end of you." The tortoise trembled in fear but said calmly, "My friend, I did not tell you to bang on the branch so violently." The baboon's anger calmed down a little but he remained as inquisitive as ever. "Hmm. Maybe it was my fault. Anyway, what are you looking at so intently?" asked the baboon. The tortoise's revenge was not complete. Quickly thinking of a plan, he said, "Friend. You are very fond of eating crickets, aren't you? I just saw one enter that hole right now," The baboon excitedly put his hand into the hole and tried to search for the cricket. A big snake came out of the hole and bit the baboon and wrapped his long body around him. The baboon screamed and roared with pain. The tortoise chuckled and said, "This is what you deserve, you lazy and greedy fellow." Since then, the tortoise, the bees and the snake had been good friends.

02 How the Dragon Came into Being

Once upon a time, there lived in a village in China, a young boy called Chang. Every morning Chang would cut some grass for the farmer's cows. One day, Chang saw some sparkling green grass in a corner of the meadow. Chang discovered that this grass would grow as soon as it was cut! Next day, Chang found a golden bead lying on the grass. He took it home and hid it in the rice jar. To his great amazement, he discovered that the next morning, the empty rice jar was full of rice. Each time he took out some rice from the jar, it would fill up again. One day, the farmer came to Chang's house with the intention of stealing the magic bead.

Chang grabbed the golden bead from him and then swallowed it! But the bead began to burn in Chang's body. He felt so hot that he drank up all the water—in the house and then in the ponds and lakes! But he still sizzled and scorched and was soon breathing fire! Chang finally turned into an entirely different creature called the dragon.

03 How the Butterflies Came into Being

A long time ago, there lived an old woman by the lakeside. She owned a garden full of pretty flowers. The fisherwomen who lived nearby was very fond of the old woman and often came to her to exchange their fish for the lovely flowers. The fisherfolk felt that there was something magical about the old woman's house. "It shines at night," someone would say. "Yes and I've even seen dwarfs dancing around her house," another would add. One day, a young couple passing by the lake stopped to admire the beautiful garden. They entered the garden to pluck some flowers but the old woman told them to go away. "Oh! How ugly the woman looks," said the man and the young couple laughed at the old woman. The old woman was furious and decided to punish them. She touched them with a cane and said, "Since you like beautiful things only, you will be turned into beautiful insects." At once, the young couple became butterflies! Whenever two lovely butterflies hover near some flowers, remember that they were once that proud couple.

04 A VOW

Once a lion killed the father of Kelly Fox and dragged the body to his cave. Kelly vowed to take revenge and hid behind a tree near the river. The lion came to know about Kelly's intention and so he did not come out of his cave. A bear came leaping up to Kelly and asked, "Brother, why are you so annoyed today?" After listening to Kelly, the bear promised to help him kill the lion. Kelly in turn promised to reward the bear with some berries and fruits. The bear raced to the lion and said, "Lord, you're the King of the Jungle. Do you know that Kelly is speaking foul about you to everyone?" On hearing this, the lion was highly annoyed and went with the bear to teach Kelly Fox a lesson. Kelly saw the lion from a distance and shot an arrow at him that pierced the lion's heart. Giving out one last roar, the lion dropped dead. Since then, the bear and the fox have been close friends.

05 The Physician's Revenge

Once the stable that housed the king's royal elephants caught fire. The king's royal physician was called to heal the elephants' wounds. On his way to the palace, the physician lay down under a tree for a nap. Suddenly, he got up with a start and realised that a crow sitting on a branch above had splattered its droppings on his face. Wiping his face, he cursed the crow and walked to the palace in a foul mood. The physician told the king to rub the elephants' wounds with crow's fat in order to heal the wounds. And so the King's men killed a large number of crows till hardly any were left. One day, a crow flew down to the king when the latter was alone and said, "Your Majesty, I have come to tell you that you are doing great injustice to us on the wrong advice of your physician. Let me tell you that crows have no fat." Hearing this, the king felt ashamed of what he had done and immediately stopped the slaughter of crows.

06 The Talkative Turtle

Once a turtle overheard two hunters planning to catch turtles the next day. The frightened turtle went to his crane friends and told them what he had heard. "Don't worry, we can take you to a safe place. But you can't fly like us," said one of the cranes. "I have a good plan", said the turtle. He suggested that the cranes would hold the two ends of a stick with their beaks while flying and he would hold the middle of the stick with his teeth. The cranes agreed but warned the turtle not to speak a word while they were flying, otherwise he would fall down and die. And so the cranes flew over rivers and hills and forests while the turtle tightly held the stick with his teeth. People who saw the unusual sight cried in wonder, "Oh! What a wonderful sight." The turtle forgot the cranes' warning and shouted in excitement, "It was my idea!" No sooner did he utter these words, his mouth lost its grip on the stick and he fell headlong onto the ground and died.

07 The Monkey's Heart

Once upon a time there was a clever monkey who lived by a river. A crocodile and his wife lived in the same river. One day, the crocodile's wife fell very ill. She wanted to eat something special. She asked her husband to get her a monkey's heart. The crocodile did not know what to do. Then he thought of his neighbour, the monkey. He said, "Friend Monkey, why do you waste your time eating the fruits of this tree? There are juicy fruits on the other side of the river." Then the monkey said that the river was too big for him to cross, the crocodile offered to take him on his back. After a while, the crocodile sank in the water along with the monkey. He told the monkey that his wife was sick and wanted his heart. The monkey realised that he had been foolish to trust the crocodile. He quickly thought of a clever plan to escape. He said, "Alas friend! Our hearts are not inside us. We have to keep them hanging on trees. I wish you had told me ear- lier. Let's go back and bring my heart." The croco- dile believed the monkey and brought him back to the tree. The monkey at once climbed up the tree and es- caped. He said to the crocodile, "You have a big body but no brains!" The crocodile had nothing to do but repent for his foolishness on being tricked by the monkey.

08 Tit for Tat

Jack and Mac were neighbours in a village. One day, Jack and his wife decided to move to the city for a better living. Before leaving, they left their ornaments and other belongings with Mac. Three years later, they returned to the village. They felt shocked and cheated to hear from Mac that their belongings had been eaten away by mice! Having thought of a plan to get back his belongings, Jack went to Mac's house a week later and requested him to look after his farm since he was not well. Mac agreed to send his son to Jack's farm. The next day, Jack's wife told Mac that an eagle had carried away his son. Mac was shocked and knew it was not possible. He understood that Jack was trying to teach him a lesson for stealing his belongings. Mac cried, "Jack, return my son to me and I promise to return your belongings." Jack came back ten minutes later with Mac's son. He was pleased to see all his belongings safe.

09 The Generous Student

Alex was known in school for being very irregular and unpunctual. The principal was fed up with his habits and decided to expel him. Alex was called to the principal's office and he arrived just when the latter was about to leave for lunch. "Is this the time to come? I sent for you an hour back. How many times do I have to tell you to be punctual?" asked the principal angrily. "Forgive me, Sir. Today I arrived late because I found a pot of gold in our field." "What? A pot of gold!" said the astounded principal. "Yes, sir!" "And what will you do with it?" said the principal, still not able to believe what he had heard. "I shall buy myself a big house with a garden, several acres of land and some I will give you for educating me." The principal was pleased and said, "Alright, I want to see that a pot of gold immediately." "Sir, it vanished as soon as my mother woke me up in the morning," answered Alex with a twinkle in his eye.

10 The Cobbler's Dream

Once there lived a poor cobbler in a small town of India. He never borrowed money from anyone and was proud of that. One night, he dreamt that he had borrowed one hundred gold coins from the moneylender. The next morning, he told his wife about his dream and soon the whole town knew about it. This news reached the greedy moneylender's ears and he went to the cobbler's house with an idea in mind. He demanded that the cobbler should return his gold coins, even though it was only a dream. The cobbler was very worried and upset and went to seek help from Birbal, the king's wise minister. After listening to the cobbler, Birbal took out hundred gold coins and placed them on a table. Then he placed a mirror in front of the coins that appeared even bigger and brighter in the reflection. The moneylender was sent for. "Here is your money", said Birbal "the ones on the table are mine and those in the reflection are yours." The moneylender was speechless and knew he had been outwitted.

11 Right Move

Once in China there lived a famous teacher called Benzei. One day, one of his pupils was caught stealing by his fellow students and they reported him to Benzei. But he remained silent and took no action against the boy. A week later, the same boy was again caught stealing. And again Benzei did nothing. Now, the other students were angry and wrote a petition to Benzei demanding for the boy's dismissal. They also threatened to leave if Benzei did not take any action against the boy this time. The teacher called his students for a meeting and said, "I know you all have not been happy with my decision. You are good boys who know the difference between right and wrong. You all can get admission in any other school. But your friend here, does not know what is right and wrong. So it's my duty to teach him instead of asking him to leave. Hearing the teacher's words tears welled up in the eyes of the boy who had stolen. He never stole again and in future became known for his honesty and integrity.

12 The Cunning Rat

There was once a rat who was very cunning. One day, when he was just about to emerge from his hole, he saw a cat waiting outside, ready to attack any rat that came out. On seeing her, the rat went back inside his hole and joined the other rats inside. Then he asked another rat who was his acquaintance, "Friend, why don't you come outside with me to the cornfields? I would enjoy the pleasure of your company. Otherwise, I would have gone alone." "Oh, sure! I shall certainly join you. Lead on, I'll follow you", said the second rat, pleased. "But how can I lead you? You are elder to me," said the first rat. And so the second rat willingly agreed to lead the way without suspecting anything fishy. Off went the two rats merrily hopping along. As soon as the second rat jumped out of the hole, the cat grabbed it and made a meal of it. The cunning rat quickly raced past the cat without being noticed.

13 The Lion and the Leopard

A long time ago, a lion and a leopard sat down and started discussing how strong they were. "No one is as strong as I. But there's one thing I really fear. He walks with two legs and carries something on his shoulder. If he takes down that thing from his shoulder, he kills something and the next moment he makes fire," said the lion. "Oh! There's nothing to fear. He dare not come near me," said the leopard confidently. Suddenly, they heard some movement in the bushes behind them. "That's him, I'm sure," said the lion in a frightened tone. "Don't be scared. Sit quietly and watch me," said the leopard. Slyly, the leopard made his way towards the hunter and as soon as he was about to leap on him, the clever hunter seized his axe, flung it down on to the leopard's head and killed him. By now, the lion was trembling with fear and had climbed onto a tree. "How awful!" he thought. Ever since, lions have been afraid of men!

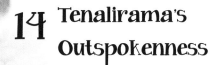

14 Tenalirama's Outspokenness

Once King Krishnadevaraya ordered the construction of a reservoir outside his palace for his subjects. He got the best of masons and within a month the reservoir was ready. The king along with his officers went to inspect the reservoir. "Wow! The reservoir is indeed well made and can store a huge amount of water," remarked the king joyfully. He then looked at his officers and asked, "What does the water in the reservoir look like?" "Oh, it's as clear as crystal," said one. "It's as pure as gold," said another to please the king. But Tenalirama spoke the truth. "The water has taken the shape of the reservoir," said Tenalirama. The king smiled and praised his pertinent remark.

15 Gasping Grasper

Once, a big miser of China was on his deathbed. Before dying, he was uncertain to which of his three sons he should hand the keys of his treasure box. He called his sons to his bedside and asked them how they would conduct his funeral. The eldest son said that he would like to give a grand funeral to his father. The miser angrily swept aside the eldest son's suggestion and said, "You fool! You will waste away all my hard earned money." The second son said, "I will call Buddhist priests only to chant prayers at your funeral. "Oh! You're as silly as your brother. Do you know how much those priests eat?" The youngest son had always hated his father's miserly habits and said in disgust, "Father, I shall spend no money on your funeral. Instead I'll dump your body in the cart and then sell it to the medical school that pays me the highest!" The miser's eyes lit up. "You're a sensible man, my son. Here, take the keys of my treasure box."

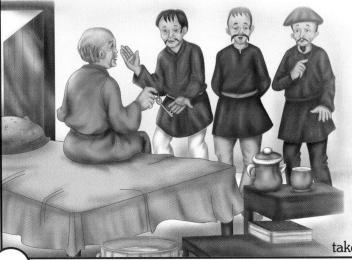

16 The Greedy Pigeon

Some birds lived together in a tree in the forest. There was a wise bird amongst them, whom the other birds addressed as Uncle Bird. One year, when it was extremely hot, Uncle Bird advised all his birds to fly to a valley near the mountains. Trusting him, all the birds found a cooler home near the mountains and lived comfortably. There was a greedy pigeon in this flock of birds. One day, she noticed a cart carrying grains to the king's palace. The pigeon hopped down onto the grains and ate to her heart's content. She was happy as she no longer had to work hard to search for food. But she advised the other birds that they should keep away from the road, as it was full of eagles and hawks. Her intention was to keep the other birds away from the grains so that she could have everything alone. One day, the pigeon was sitting on the road when the cart came speeding down and hit the pigeon, crushing the greedy pigeon to death.

17 The Bad Tempered Princess

Once a Sultan had a very beautiful daughter called Salma. Salma was very ill-tempered and proud. So no prince was willing to marry her. On Salma's seventeenth birthday, a young and handsome man came to the Sultan's court and asked him if he could paint the princess' portrait. The young artist put forth a condition. "No one will be allowed to see the portrait until it is completed." Finally, the day arrived when the portrait was to be to be shown to a large gathering. The audience gave out a gasp of shock on seeing the portrait. The princess was shown with her long hair in disorder, a terrible scowl on her face and an angry look in the eyes. "That's how the princess actually looks most of the time," cried out somebody from the audience. The princess was stunned and ashamed to hear this and realised that it was because of her ill temper and rude behaviour that she appeared so in the portrait. From that day, the princess changed into a new person— sweet tempered and sensible.

18 The Magical Storm

A poor farmer owned a fertile piece of land that reaped huge harvests. He soon gathered a lot of wealth and money, but left his poor parents to fend for themselves. When they approached him for money and food, he refused. "Go away. I have nothing to spare," he said. The old couple left in tears. On their way back, they met an elf who gave them a big loaf of bread and some milk to drink. After they drank the milk, something very unusual happened. Suddenly, it became dark and a fierce storm blew across the town. Instead of their small hut, there stood a huge mansion. The couple stood astounded and raced at once to share the unbelievable news with their son. When they reached the farm, they found their son sitting in a state of shock and cursing his fate. The fertile land was no longer there. Instead, it lay covered with stones and rubble. The parents consoled their son and took him to their new house. The guilty son begged his parents to forgive him for his ungrateful behaviour.

19 Tenalirama Subjugates a Wrestler's Arrogance

Atisura, a famous wrestler, once came to King Krishnadevrai's kingdom and challenged the royal wrestlers. Aware of Atisura's fame, the royal wrestlers were very worried. Tenalirama decided to fight Atisura. Assuming the name of Virakesari, Tenalirama borrowed the wrestlers badges, wore them and went to meet Atisura in Krishnadevrai's court. He then challenged Atisura to tell the meaning of some symbols which he would show. If Atisura failed, he would have to accept defeat and leave. Atisura agreed and Tenalirama showed some symbols with his palm and fingers, holding Atisura's neck. Atisura tried his level best to interpret them, but failed to understand that Tenalirama meant who would take care of his family when Atisura would wrestle him to death. Thus, Atisura had to accept defeat before witty Tenalirama and leave.

20 The Sleepy Teacher

Once there lived a teacher who loved taking a short nap every afternoon after the lunch break. Every day, after coming to the class, he would set some tasks for his students and then he would sit on his chair, rest his feet on the table and go to sleep. One day, some students asked him, "Sir, why do you take this short nap every afternoon?" "Oh, actually, I go to Dreamland to meet some ancient sages," said he, checking the copies the students had submitted. On one extremely sultry afternoon, some of the students dozed off while the teacher was taking their class. He woke them up and chided them for their indiscipline. "We went to the dreamland, sir", said the students, "and we talked to the ancient sages." "Ah-ha! OK, so what did they say?" the teacher demanded to know. "We asked them whether any school teacher came every afternoon, but they said they had seen no such person. Maybe they forgot, sir!"

21 The Unwelcome Guests

Peter was poor, but he loved inviting people to his house. It meant a hard time for his wife. One day, while looking out of the window, the woman saw three men coming towards their house. Her husband was out and she took this opportunity to avoid these unwanted guests. When they arrived, she greeted them warmly. They entered the house and found that a mortar and a pestle were made ready for worship at one side of the room. They got very puzzled. The woman saw their faces and asked, "Don't you know my husband worships mortar and pestle? This rite needs human blood. My husband will hit you on your head with this pestle to draw blood. I hate this. After all, I have to clean up the whole mess afterwards," said she in a matter-of-fact tone. Just then, Peter arrived. He was surprised to see his guests running past him. "They wanted the pestle but I refused," explained his wife. Hearing this, Peter took the pestle and rushed to give it to them. Seeing him coming with the pestle, the guests ran fast for their lives.

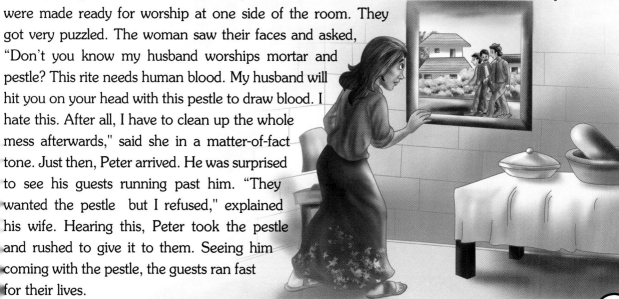

22 Costly Gifts

One day, a man visited the king of the land with a fat chicken in his hand. He said, "Your Majesty! I gambled in your name and won this chicken. Please accept this." The king happily accepted it and asked him to hand it over to his poultry keeper. A few days later he came again, this time with a goat and the same story. The king accepted this too and sent it to his goatkeeper. A few days later, the man came again. But this time, he brought no gifts. Instead, he had two men with him. The king asked him the reason for this visit. "Your Majesty! Yesterday I was gambling with these men in your name. But this time I lost five hundred gold coins to each of them. I don't have money to pay them," replied the gambler with a sorry face. The king realised that he made a mistake by accepting those gifts on the previous occasions. So, this time he could not refuse to pay him. He paid off the two men and warned the gambler never to play in his name.

23 The Crocodile and the Dog

A long time back, the dog had a big mouth and a short tongue which was too small for his mouth. So, the dog had a lot of trouble while speaking. He had a crocodile friend who too had a big mouth. But his tongue was long enough to fit his mouth. One day he was expecting some guests in his house. But he was embarrassed about making his speech. He went to the crocodile and said, "Friend, I will have some important guests today in my house. You know, my words don't come clear. Would you please give me your tongue for today? I will return it to you as soon as they leave. Meanwhile, you can use my tongue." The crocodile had no problem with this arrangement and lent him his tongue. The dog had a lovely time with his guests. He felt so comfortable talking with the crocodile's tongue that he did not feel like giving it back. So when the crocodile asked for his tongue back, he simply refused to return it. Since then, crocodiles and dogs have been enemies.

24 King Shibi

King Shibi was a noble and charitable king. One day, he was in his court when a dove flew in and took refuge in his lap. "Please save me from my enemy. The hawk will kill me." The hawk followed the dove. He demanded his prey back. "I earned it after hard labour. I am hungry. You have no right to take my food." The king pleaded with him to spare the dove. After many requests, the hawk said, "I can leave my claim over the dove only if you cut out your flesh equal to the weight of the dove." The king readily agreed. He put the dove on one side of the scale and started cutting his flesh to weigh it against the dove. But the weight of the dove kept increasing. And lo! To

his surprise, there was no hawk or dove. Instead, standing in front of him were two angels who made his body as it was before. They blessed him and said, "Your name shall be remembered as long as the world lasts."

25 Interdependence

Deep inside a dense forest, some pine trees were having an early morning conversation. One young pine tree said, "Enough is enough! Animals come and rest under our shade but leave a lot of mess behind. The stench is really unbearable. I have made up my mind to drive away any animal who comes here to take rest", "I feel that it's not a wise thing to do," said the oldest tree of the forest. "I can understand your problem. But try to adjust. We are all interdependent trees, men, animals...." "I'm sorry, sir" interrupted the aggressive one. "I respect your views. But in this matter, I am not going to take anybody's advice." From that day, he started frightening animals away by shaking violently. In course of time, animals stopped coming there altogether. One day, two woodcutters came in the forest. "Men!" cried the aggressive pine. "You can well guess why they have come," said the oldest pine. "Earlier they never came here because of the wild animals. Now in their absence..." The aggressive pine began to shiver. It was the first one to be cut down.

26 Temper

One day, a bad-tempered priest, while enjoying his daily meal, noticed a strand of hair in his curry. He hollered at his wife, "If ever I see a hair in my curry again, I will shave off your head." The wife cooked all the more carefully. But still after a few days, the priest spotted another strand of hair in his food. The angry priest took his razor and ran after his wife to shave her head off. The woman was scared to death and locked herself in the kitchen. Her screams and the priest's bellowing voice reached their neighbours and they poured in to see what had happened. Someone went to call Raja Birbal. Hearing everything, Raja Birbal reached the place with what seemed like a funeral procession. He inquired of the priest, "Who has died? I heard that your wife was going to shave off her head. That's why I thought it must be you since only widows shave off their heads." "He'll have to die first. But then he can't shave her head by his own hand," quipped a little boy. The priest realised his mistake and promised to control his rage in future.

27 The Diplomatic Reply

One day, Lion King called all his subjects to his cave. A bear, feeling nauseated by the stench, held a handkerchief to his nose. The king, feeling offended, knocked him down. "Does my court smell bad?" asked the lion. A monkey, trying to please him said, "No, Your Majesty! It smells like a bunch of roses." The king knew this was not the case and the monkey faced the same fate as the bear. "Let me have some other opinions," said the lion aloud. The fox was actually trying to creep out of the cave. "You fox! No way you can try to escape my eyes," growled the king. He too was holding a handkerchief to his nose. The other animals looked at each other's faces. "What do you have to say about the smell of my court?" asked the lion sternly. "Your Highness, I have a terrible cold," the fox pretended to sneeze. "I cannot smell a thing so I can't say how your court smells." The side of the lion's lips broke into a smile. He liked this reply and gave the fox an important post in the court.

28 The Hermit

Emperor Akbar was always engrossed in thought about his empire. Raja Birbal felt concerned about him. One day, the emperor was strolling in his garden, when he spotted an old hermit lying in his garden. Akbar yelled at him, "Hey, fellow! What are you doing in my garden?" The man opened his eyes and sat up. "Sir, is this your garden?" asked he. "Of course, it is! This garden is mine. The courtyard, the palace, the fort, the whole empire is mine," the emperor was visibly irritated. "Ah! And before you, sir, whom did this garden, fort and city belong to?" "My father, of course!" replied Akbar. "And who owned these before him?" the man asked. "My grandfather." "So, sir, there was always someone before you and there will be someone else after you. When you die, nothing belongs to you. Don't you think we are all like travellers resting in this world, which is like an inn on the pathway?" "Yes, it is! You have opened my eyes," said Akbar, realising the basic truth of life. The man removed his false white beard and there stood Birbal smiling.

29 How Man Got Fire

Mantis, the Creator, felt that mankind was not ready for fire. So he entrusted the ostrich to keep it under one of its wings. Learning this, a Bushman thought, "Why didn't the Creator give us the fire. We too need it badly," and planned to steal it from the ostrich. He went up to him and said, "I dreamt something about you. If you stand with your wings spread out in the strong wind before dawn, you will soar into the sky like an eagle." "Really!" said the ostrich excitedly. It had been his dream to fly like an eagle. Next day, just before dawn, the ostrich spread its wings and waited, expecting to soar into the sky. As he waited, the Bushman tiptoed towards him, grabbed the fire and ran away.

30 Wisdom and Wealth

One day, Wisdom and Wealth started on a journey to search for a home. On their way, they came across a man sitting under a tree. "Where are you two going?" inquired the man. "We are looking for a place to live," said Wealth. "Well, in that case I would like you to stay with me," said the man. "No, Sir, I can't go with you since without Wisdom you'll not be able to keep me with you for ever," explained Wealth. Saying this they set off again. On their way they met another man. They asked him whether he knew any place where they could live. The man said, "Well, I can keep Wisdom with me." Wisdom agreed and Wealth followed him.

31 The Fire Specialists

In an enormous haystack, a tortoise, a cobra, a mongoose and a jackal made their homes. The four animals were great friends. All the three animals, except the fox considered themselves to be very knowledgeable and were very proud of their wisdom. Often, they boast together singing:

We are the wise three

Do come and seek our advice for free

There's nothing that we don't know

Do you want us to show?

One day, while they were lazing, they heard people screaming, "Fire! Fire in the haystack! Douse the flames with water..." "Fire? I know a hundred thousand ways of dealing with it," said the tortoise boastfully. "And I know a thousand ways", added the cobra arrogantly. "I know only a few hundred," said the mongoose. Then they turned towards the jackal and asked, "And how many methods do you know?" "Only one", said the jackal sniffing the air. "When the fire is this close, there is only one way to escape: Run!" Saying this he leaped out of the haystack and fled. "Poor soul"… mocked the tortoise. But, before he could finish, a giant flame swallowed him and his knowledgeable friends.

Contents

The Story of the Month: The Tea Kettle of Good Luck

The Story of the Month

The Tea Kettle of Good Luck

September

01 The Tea Kettle of Good Luck

A long time ago, an old monk bought a beautiful tea pot and took it home with him to the monastery. He was a tea lover and immediately set the tea pot on the flame to make some tea. "Ouch! It's hot!" shouted the tea pot and jumped off the hearth. The monk was so scared seeing this unusual activity that he decided to get rid of the tea pot.

"I need to sell this unusual tea pot at whatever price I get before it harms me," thought the monk and sold it off to a poor peddler for a meagre sum. The peddler was unaware why the monk had sold off such a beautiful tea pot and took it home happily. He kept it near his bed and went off to sleep. Suddenly, a scratching sound awoke him. The peddler could not believe what he saw—the tea pot was moving around with furry legs, a head and a tail! "Good gracious! Who are you?" shouted the peddler. "I'm a badger but I am called the Tea Kettle of Good Luck. I bring good luck to whoever owns me, provided I'm not put on the flame," said the badger. The badger then started dancing and singing merrily, hopping all over the room. The peddler was amused with

the tea pot's dance and said, "Ok, I'll never put you on the flame." He then began to make arrangements for a public show, where the tea pot could perform his tricks and show off his dancing skills.

The next day, the peddler constructed a large stage and announced that the strange tea pot would put up a unique show. Out of curiosity, the people came to see if the peddler was true to his word. The tea pot performed his acrobatic feats and entertaining dances. The people were so amused that huge crowds started visiting the peddler's house daily, paying a good price to watch the tea pot's wondrous and amusing feats. In no time the news spread and the peddler made huge profits staging the tea pot's shows.

One day, the peddler went up to the tea pot and said, "Friend, I've got enough wealth now. You must be tired of your performances and need rest. Let's stop these public shows." The tea pot smiled and said, "As you wish. I'm glad that you are still as humble as you were before. All these riches have not made you greedy."

The peddler then wrapped the tea pot in a piece of linen and took the tea pot to the old monk in the monastery. He bowed before the monk and said, "Your Reverence, I've come to return you the fortune you had given me. This Kettle of Good Luck belongs to you. I've got enough wealth to last me for a lifetime.

Please do take back your fortune." He narrated the amazing story of the tea pot to the monk. The other monks in the monastery were amazed to hear the strange tale about the tea pot and said, "Let's preserve this unusual tea pot in the monastery and treat it with the respect it deserves." So they kept it on a shelf, wrapped in silk and preserved it with all the other treasures.

02 The Strange Creature

Zoro, was an obedient boy, yet his aunt kept nagging and yelling at him all day long. One day, she sent him to the forest to get some wild berries inspite of knowing that the forest was inhabited by a man eater. Zoro reluctantly obeyed. While he was gathering the berries, the monster appeared and rushed at Zoro to gobble him up. Zoro at once took out his drum and started beating it loudly. Hearing the drum beats, the monster started dancing till he was tired and went off to sleep. Zoro returned home and told his aunt what had happened. But she refused to believe him. The next day, the entire family went to the forest to see whether there really was a monster. They reached the forest and after a while the huge monster appeared and gobbled up Zoro's father, mother and his aunt. It then rushed towards Zoro. Seeing this, Zoro took out his drum and started beating it fast. As soon as the monster started dancing, he spat out Zoro's father, his mother and then his aunt. Zoro kept beating his drum till the beast fell down dead from sheer exhaustion. His family had looked on in fear and amazement. They had all learnt their lesson, especially Zoro's aunt. From then on, his aunt stopped nagging Zoro and they lived happily as a family, trusting and believing each other and tried not to be unkind to anyone.

03 Ways to Bathe

One hot summer day, a goose set out to look for some water. On the way, he met a chicken and a cat and together they headed to the Great Lake singing merrily:

One, two, three
Here we go on a swimming spree
We'll play and swim for free
Under the shade of the Banyan tree

On reaching the lake, the three of them jumped headlong into the water. While the goose flapped his wings in joy and waddled in the water, the chicken and the cat almost got drowned. They somehow managed to climb to the shore and promising never to venture out into the water. Then returned home. On the way, the chicken saw some golden sand and decided to have a sand bath, while the cat, who was shivering, sat atop a stove and licked himself all over.

04 The Lazy Apprentice

Long ago, there lived a girl in a forest who worked as an apprentice to the Goddess of Weaving. The girl was lazy and did not enjoy working hard. One day, the goddess asked her to prepare a dress by cleaning some cotton, beating it, spinning it, weaving it into cloth, cutting it, and finally sewing it. The girl felt too lazy to work so hard for a dress and thought, "Why should I slog so much over a dress. I can very well wear the leather cloth used to beat the cotton. It will be more lasting." Thinking so, the girl did not do any cleaning or spinning and wore the leather like a dress. Seeing this, the Goddess of Weaving was infuriated. She at once called the girl and said, "You've disobeyed me. You shall now pay a heavy price for your laziness." Saying so, the goddess punished the sluggish girl by making the leather stick to her skin, and by attaching the beating stick to her body.

05 The Royal Servant

Kamera, a prosperous kingdom in Africa, was ruled by a proud King. One day, the king sat on his royal stool in his mud palace and declared, "I'm the Master of the World and all the people are my servants." While the others nodded in agreement, a frail voice from the crowd shouted, "No, we're all each others' servants." This annoyed the king and he demanded, "Who dares to disagree with me?" There was utter silence in the courtroom as an old man stepped forward. He bowed before the king and said, "Your Majesty, I'll prove my point before nightfall". The old man then asked the king to hold his staff while he touched the king's feet. The king did as he was asked and after touching his feet, the old man said, "Here you are, My Lord. You have acted exactly the way I asked you to. So, we are all each others servants, aren't we?" King Sultan was pleased with the old man's wit and made him his royal advisor.

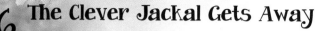

06 The Clever Jackal Gets Away

One hot summer afternoon, a clever jackal was wandering through a narrow rocky pass near the forest looking for some food. Suddenly, he realised that the lion was walking ahead of him. 'Oh no, it's the lion. He'll kill me if he sees me for I have played a number of tricks on him. I need to do something to escape," he thought to himself. The clever jackal looked up towards the cliff and started shouting, "Help! Help!" The lion heard the jackal's cry and came running. "What happened? Why are you yelling, sly jackal?" enquired the lion. The jackal at once implored, "O King of the Forest, our lives are in danger as these rocks from the cliff can roll down any moment and crush us. Only you can stop this calamity." Flattered by the jackal's praise, the lion stood with his back to the cliff as if holding on to the rocks and the great cliff on his shoulders. The sly jackal walked away with the pretext of going to look for aid.

07 The Witch in the Tower

Long ago, the citizens of the Japanese city of Kyoto were very terrified by a witch who capsized the city gates and lived in the city tower. Many a brave samurai died fighting against the wicked witch who stabbed them with her flying sword. The citizens longed for a samurai like Watanabi, who had earlier saved Kyoto from all evils. Watanabi's son heard of the troubles about the witch and decided to fight back the wicked witch. The young boy picked up Watanabi's sword and left for the city tower. When the witch saw the boy approaching, she grinned to see such a young enemy and did not prepare to fight him. The little boy climbed up the tower silently and before the witch could react, he stabbed her with the same flying sword that she had used to terrorize the people of Kyoto with. The wicked witch lay dead and thus Watanabi's son saved Kyoto and its people.

08 Mike and the Golden Deer

Mike, the son of a rich merchant wasted his wealth in gambling and drinking till at last he was left with nothing. Unable to pay his debts, Mike decided to drown himself. The golden deer who lived in the nearby grove, saw Mike and saved him, asking him never to reveal to anyone who had saved his life. Mike went home, thanking the deer. One day, the queen dreamed about the golden deer and expressed her desire to have it. The king announced a huge reward to the one who could bring him the golden deer. "This is an opportunity to be rich again," thought Mike and went to the palace. He told the king about the golden deer's abode. The king brought the golden deer to the palace and kept it in the palace gardens. But he banished Mike for betraying the golden deer's trust.

09 The Mysterious Tracks

A villager once saw huge round footmarks in the courtyard. "Good gracious! What's this?" thought the shocked villager and ran to inform the village chief. The villagers came running to see the unusual tracks. "This must be the foot marks of a demon," said the village chief and the villagers started to panic. But Milan, the so-called wise man of the village was not convinced and declared those to be the footprints of a deer, unaware that they were an elephant's footprints. "Deer! But they are so big…" asked the village chief hesitatingly. Milan smiled and said, "Oh! That's because the deer tied large stones to its feet to fool us." Everyone praised Milan's wits. The villagers then went back to their homes feeling relieved that it was no demon. After a few days, similar footprints were seen but the villagers were not scared for they were sure as Milan had said that those were the tracks of the deer.

10 The Golden Touch

King Midas was a devout man. Pleased with his devotion, the God of Riches appeared before Midas in his dream and said, "Tell me what you wish. I shall grant whatever you wish for," Midas's greatest obsession was gold and he at once said, "All that I touch should turn into solid gold," The God granted his wish and whatever Midas touched the next morning, turned into gold. Midas's joy knew no bounds. But when Midas hugged his loving daughter, Rosemary and she turned into gold, Midas wept aloud, "Take this curse away and give my daughter back in flesh and blood." At last, the God of Riches appeared before him. "What is it that you desire now?" asked the God. Midas fell to his knees and begged the God of Riches to take away the boon he had granted him at first and to return his daughter to him. The God of Riches did as Midas had asked and vanished. Midas was happy to get his daughter and never ever craved for gold.

11 The Poet's Reward

A poet once wrote a poem in praise of the king. The king was so pleased with it that he decided to give the poet a handsome reward. "Tell me what you want," declared the king. The poet very humbly bowed his head and said, "Your Majesty, give me a hound." Everyone was shocked to hear the poet. The king granted the poet's wish. The poet gladly accepted the hound and said, "It would be nice if I can have a horse to go hunting with the hound." The king fulfilled his wish and then the poet very cleverly asked for a cook to cook the game for him. Not yet satisfied, the poet very cleverly said, "I'm worried where I will accommodate my rewards. My house is quite small," At this the king gave the poet a mansion and a date plantation to bear the expenses of maintaining his estate. "You are great, Your Highness!" cheered the poet and left leaving everybody dumbfounded. The crafty poet had got what he wanted, yet he had given the king the impression that he was not a greedy man by not asking for everything at once.

12 The Irreverent Devotee

Tenalirama was an ardent devotee of Goddess Kali. Pleased with his devotion, the goddess appeared before him one day, sporting a thousand faces. Tenalirama bowed with devotion but suddenly burst out laughing. Unable to understand the reason behind Tenlirama's laughter, the goddess enquired what had happened. Tenalirama joined his hands and said, "Mother, I was just thinking that I have one nose and yet I'm in a terrible state when I get a cold. I was wondering what your plight would be in such a situation, with a thousand noses," Tenalirama's wit and audacity pleased the goddess and she decided to reward him. She held out two crucibles of nectar— one was the crucible of Wealth and the other was the crucible of Wisdom. The goddess asked Tenalirama to dip his fingers into any one of them. But, before the goddess could react, Tenalirama immediately dipped his fingers into both and the goddess had no choice but to grant him both Wisdom and Wealth.

13 The Monkey's Trial

Once two cats, Harry and Teddy saw a piece of delicious cake on a bench and decided to take it for themselves. But, instead of trying to share it, each claimed to have seen the piece of cake first and tried to keep it for himself. They started arguing.

"Let's go to the monkey's court and ask him to decide who will get the bigger share," suggested Teddy and the two cats hurried to the monkey's court, still arguing over the piece of cake. The monkey heard them and felt tempted to eat the piece of cake himself. He took the piece of cake and divided it into two. But one half was bigger than the other. The monkey took a bite from the bigger half to try and make them equal. Now, the other half became bigger. So the monkey took another bite from the bigger half. In this way, the monkey went on taking one bite after another from the two halves, pretending to make them equal, till at last, the pieces became quite tiny. "Now," announced the monkey, "I'll have these small pieces as my fees", and chased Harry and Teddy away."

14 The Greatest Fool

Every year as a part of Holi celebrations, King Krishnadevaraya held a show where he selected the 'greatest fool' of the year. At this show, people used to try and outdo each other in acting in a funny and peculiar way. Tenalirama, won this hilarious competition almost every year. The other courtiers were unhappy at Tenali's success. Once, they managed to prevent Tenali from joining the event by drugging him. When the effects of the drug wore off, Tenali rushed to join the event but was very late. As soon as he reached the venue of the event, the king got furious. "You fool! You have come just before the completion of the event. I haven't seen a greater fool than you," shouted the king angrily. But to everyone's amazement, Tenalirama smiled and said, "Thanks a lot, Your Majesty for choosing me the greatest fool again. Where is my award?" The king burst into peals of laughter and Tenali got his rewards.

15 The Precious Present

Long ago, in a remote village, the poor villagers found a gold coin and decided that it must be gifted to the king as a token of their gratitude. So, the innocent villagers made a grand palanquin and placed the coin inside it. Four very traditionally dressed, healthy youths of the village, accompanied by the headman carried the palanquin to the palace. The path was far from smooth and as the palanquin bumped along on their shoulders, the coin fell out. No one seemed to have noticed and the party went along to the king's palace. The villagers were treated as royal guests but when they went to present the gift to the king, it was nowhere to be found in the palanquin. The poor villagers hung their heads in shame. "You rustics, you came to fool us!" shouted the angry courtiers. But, the wise king could see their innocence and sent them back to their village with many gifts.

16 A Tale of Two Heads

A merchant from Damascus went to Troy to trade. He was a middle-aged man with handsome looks but a bald head. One day, while he was standing in the market place trading his goods, he met a Trojan scholar. They got along very well and developed a bond of friendship. The scholar invited the merchant to his house for dinner saying, "Friend, you'll be leaving our town soon. Please do come over for dinner tonight." The merchant obliged and dressed in his finest outfit, went to the scholar's house. The merchant was warmly welcomed by the scholar's wife. The dining table was filled with sumptuous dishes. When the merchant was about to leave, the scholar picked up a brass pot from the table and showing its base to the merchant asked, "Friend, why do you Damascenes have heads like this?" The merchant understood that the scholar meant his bald head and promptly replied, turning the pot upright and showing the empty cavity, "Why do you Trojans have heads like this?" The two friends had a good laugh and went their own way.

17 Half Hungry

Rambo, a poor farmer was destined to always remain hungry. One day, Rambo was invited to a rich man's daughter's wedding. As Rambo sat down to have his food, the God of Destiny took the form of a frog and jumped onto Rambo's plate. Rambo was short sighted and swallowed the frog with the food. Feeling trapped, the God of Destiny asked Rambo to spit him out but Rambo refused. At last Rambo agreed to spit out the frog on condition that the curse of hunger would be removed from him. The god agreed saying that Rambo would have to worship him with true devotion. Rambo spat out the frog and asked how he could worship the God of Destiny with true devotion. Taking his original form, the god said, "Be under the curse of hunger," and disappeared.

18 The Ox, the Ram and the Cock

An ox was very proud of his strength and ran away from his master's house to live an independent life. All throughout summer he enjoyed, but when winter came he started shivering in the bitter cold. So he decided to go to a warmer land. On his way, he met a ram who had escaped his mean owner and now joined him in his journey. All along they sang merrily:

Here we march like a band

On our way to a warmer land

No more chilly nights

We'll graze in bright daylight

A cock heard them and joined them too. In the evening, they heard a loud call and looked overhead to see a flight of geese travelling south. The three travellers asked a gander if they too could go with them. The gander refused saying they would take ages to develop wings and fly so high and therefore, suggested that they should go back to their masters. The three friends then decided that they would live there together and start a new life with each other as good friends.

19 How the Dog Found Himself a Master

Long ago, when dogs were independent creatures like wolves, a dog decided to take the strongest being on earth as his master. He set out in search for a master and met a fierce wolf on the way whom he accepted as his master. But when the wolf saw a bear, he ran away and the dog decided to serve the bear instead. "Let's go hunting," suggested the bear and went deep into the forest with the dog. "Roarrr…" they heard a loud cry. The bear at once said, "Hide, else the lion will kill us." Seeing him scared, the dog decided to leave the bear and serve the lion, the king of beasts as his master. So he bid farewell to the bear and went along with the lion. The dog lived happily with the lion for sometime till one day the lion saw a man in the forest and fled. This made the dog realise that humans are stronger than all beasts and from then on, dogs serve men.

20 The Antelope and the Goat's Farm

Once an antelope and a goat decided to farm together and sowed beans and corns. They worked hard but when the harvest time came, the antelope came and picked all the beans leaving nothing for the goat. Quite depressed, the goat asked God how she could get her share of the beans. God promised her to make many more beans so that she could have plenty of them. Feeling happy the goat sang:

Hurrah! I'll have beans in plenty

My granary will be the biggest in the county

I'll be rich now

And before me all will bow

The goat then picked baskets full of beans. The antelope saw this and came to ask her share. She invited the wild cat to divide their shares. The wild cat brought huge baskets for himself and the antelope but a small one for the goat. Seeing this, the goat asked two wild dogs to help her. The wild dogs ate up the unjust wild cat and chased the antelope away, leaving all the beans for the goat.

21 Horse Play

Tenalirama and the king were once passing by the riverside. Tenalirama was riding a lean and thin horse while the king was riding an Arabian stud. "Look how healthy and handsome my horse is!" boasted the king. Tenalirama looked at the king's stallion and said that the king's strong stallion would not be able to do feats which his shabby horse could. At this, the king burst out laughing and asked how his lean and thin horse was extraordinary. Tenalirama kept quiet for a while and then rode straight into the river. He drowned his horse in the water and said, "My Lord, can your horse do this?" The king was taken aback for he could not dare to drown his handsome stallion and thus, he had to accept the superiority of Tenalirama's horse.

22 Milk for the Mullah

A man once came to Mullah Naseeruddin seeking advice. "What's the matter?" asked the Mullah, staring at the milk can in the man's hand. The man heaved a sigh and said, "I have a serious problem. I don't drink wine but every morning when I wake up, I feel intoxicated."

The Mullah thought for a moment and said, "Hmmm… it's indeed a matter of concern. What do you drink last thing at night?" The man replied humbly that he drank a glass of milk every night before going to bed. "That's where the problem is!" shouted the Mullah. The man wore a surprised look on his face and asked, "Is milk intoxicating?" The Mullah then very wittily explained how the milk inside the stomach gets churned when one tosses in bed and turns into butter and the butter in turn becomes cheese, the cheese turns into fat, fat becomes sugar and finally sugar becomes alcohol. Hearing him, the man gave away the can of milk to Mullah and left, promising never to drink milk at night.

23 The Lion and the Mosquitoes

A lion once got up from a deep sleep and stretching himself boasted of his strength saying, "No one can harm me but the poor mosquitoes can be killed by anybody." A swarm of mosquitoes heard him and was annoyed. "Look! How proud the lion is," said the mosquitoes and decided to teach the vain lion a lesson. So they all flew towards the lion and started biting him. The lion tried to save himself by rolling on the ground and slapping them with his paws. Unable to bear it any longer, the lion pleaded, "Please do spare me. I never intended to make fun of your strength." The mosquitoes at last took pity on the proud lion and left saying, "All right, we'll spare you. But remember not to look down upon others and think yourself to be the ultimate power." The lion felt ashamed of himself and agreed never to behave in that manner again.

24 Family Misfortunes

The Dough Family consisted of Father Dough, Mother Butter, Daughter Cotton and Son Ant. One morning, mother Butter asked Ant to get some dried resins for fuel, warning him not to go near fresh resins as he might get stuck. 'I'm not a kid,' thought Ant and jauntily went up the Mepche tree and got stuck. When Ant did not return for a long time, Father Dough decided to go in search of him. "Don't walk on the edge of the road," warned his wife. But Mr. Dough was too proud to listen to his wife and walked so near the edge that he slipped and rolled down. Mrs. Dough then asked Cotton to go and look for her brother and father. "Remember not to walk in open space, else you'll be carried away," warned Mother Butter. Cotton too did not listen and was carried away by a gust of strong wind. Mrs. Butter then came out to look for her family herself. Not realising how hot it was, she melted in the scorching heat, bringing the Dough Family to an end!

25 King of the Birds

The fish eagle once called a meeting of all the birds to decide who could be a ruler among them. They decided to gather in the open field the day after the full moon and fly high up the sky to touch the hand of God. Whosoever did that first, would be the ruler. So on the appointed day, all the birds gathered as decided. The swallow hid under the fish eagle's huge feathers and flew a long distance without any effort. So, while the others were tired, the swallow flew ahead of the others. Knowing that he had cheated, the other birds chased the swallow to punish him. The swallow hid in a snake hole while the owl guarded the hole the entire night. But the owl fell asleep and the swallow sneaked out of the hole and flew away, safe and escaped punishment. The other birds were so angry with the owl for letting the swallow get away that they cursed it. They said that from then on, the owl would never be able to sleep at night. And so it remains till this day. The owl never sleeps at night.

26 Why Trees Whisper

When men were forced to leave Paradise, a man went deep into the forest to make his home. He came to a grove of Pine, Spruce and Alder trees. The man raised his axe to cut some pinewood. "Oh no, see the sticky tears flowing out of me and have mercy on me," said the Pine tree. The man reluctantly went to the Spruce tree and decided to cut it. "Please spare me. My wood will be of no use. It's dried and twisted," pleaded the Spruce tree. The man then tried cutting the Alder tree but it also discouraged the man saying, "Don't cut me and let me bleed to death." Quite frustrated, the man prayed to God asking for a way to get some wood to build his house. Hearing him, God took pity on him and ordered all the trees to allow the man to cut as much wood he wanted. The man then gathered the wood from the trees and built his shelter. And forever again, chopped down any and every tree to fulfil his wishes and desires. That is why trees still get restless and begin to whisper when a man enters the forest.

27 The Test

One day, a schoolmaster was attacked by a gang of dacoits. On knowing that he was a teacher, the dacoit chief decided to test his skills. He handed the teacher a pumpkin and asked him to guess its exact weight, threatening to give him a hundred lashes if he failed. The teacher was a clever man. He took the pumpkin in his hand and said very thoughtfully, "Here you are. This pumpkin weighs the same as your head." Now the chief's head needed to be weighed to test if the teacher's statement was correct. This was possible only if his head was separated from his body. Sensing danger, the chief laughed out and pretending to have played a joke on the teacher, allowed him to go unharmed.

28 The King of Fruits

Gopal the royal jester was known for his enormous appetite. One day, a rich landlord invited him for lunch. Gopal ate as much as three people and burped aloud declaring that he had no place left in his stomach for any more food. Just then a servant came in with a plate of mango slices and Gopal ate it all. "Amazing! You said you had no place left in you stomach," said the astounded landlord. "What happens when a king walks into a crowded room? Everybody steps aside to let him in. Similarly, since the mango is the king of fruits, all the food in my stomach made the way for it," replied Gopal sheepishly.

29 Super Salesman

For a long time, Mullah Naseeruddin had been trying to sell his house, without any success. One day, he took an old axe and hit the wall of the house with all his might. Hearing the sound, his wife came running out of the kitchen. She was appalled to see Mulla hitting at the wall with an axe. "Have you gone crazy?" she asked, holding his hand back. "Oh, foolish woman!" said Naseeruddin. "I am just trying to take a brick. Nowadays, to sell anything, you have to first show a sample of it. I'll show this brick as a sample of our house and then I shall be able to sell it," said the hapless man.

30 The Mouse Deer and the Crocodile

One day, a mouse deer had to cross the river to collect his food. But, there were crocodiles in the river and so he made a plan. "Crocodile King," he called out. "The king has asked me to count all the crocodiles in this river. So ask all your clan's crocodiles to line up from this side of the river to the other." The crocodile did as asked. The mouse deer jumped onto the crocodile's back, one after the other and crossed the river. "How many are we?" the crocodile yelled. "Just enough to cross the river," said the mouse deer and laughed.

Contents

The Story of the Month: Tenalirama in Babur's Court

The Story of the Month

Tenalirama in Babur's Court

01 Tenalirama in Babur's Court

The stories of Tenalirama's intelligence and wit spread far and wide. When Emperor Babur heard of Tenalirama's wit, he expressed his utmost desire to meet Tenalirama. So he sent a messenger to King Krishnadevaraya to invite Tenalirama to his court. Maharaja Krishnadevaraya readily accepted the request and sent for Tenali. When Tenali came, the king said, "Tenali! Now is the moment to show your real intelligence. The Mughal emperor has sent for you, hearing about your intelligence. The honour and pride of our state lie on your shoulder." Tenali promised the king that he would not let him down and set out for Delhi. Meanwhile, Babur had warned his courtiers against laughing, even if Tenali said the most amusing thing. When Tenali reached the capital, he was warmly greeted but no one smiled. For the next two weeks, Tenali said many things amusing enough to make one burst into fits of laughter, but no one even smiled. Tenali understood that all the people were deliberately somber only to show him down. But Tenali was not the person who would accept defeat so easily. He made a different plan. Every day Babur would go for an early morning walk by the bank of the river Jamuna. A minister carrying a small bag of gold coins always accompanied him. The emperor used to give these gold coins to the beggars and other needy persons he would come across. One day, Tenali dressed as an old sadhu, carrying a spade over his shoulder and a mango sapling in his hand, waited for Babur. When he saw the emperor approaching, he started digging out the ground as if preparing to plant the sapling. Babur was surprised to see an old man planting a mango sapling. He went up to him and asked, "My dear old man! What will you do by planting this sapling? You are so old. By the time, this sapling grows into a tree and bears fruits, you won't be there. I am not planting it for myself. I enjoyed the fruits of trees planted by my father. Now, those who will live after

me shall enjoy the fruits of trees enjoyed planted by me. " This is so satisfying," said Tenali disguised. Babur liked his thoughts. "You're a great man. I admire your views. Take these gold coins and plant more such saplings." Accepting the award, Tenali bowed reverentially and said, "May God give you a long life! You see, normally people get fruits after many years of planting but I have got it so soon. It proves that consideration for others reaps a rich harvest," Babur was fascinated by these words as well and gave him more coins. Again, Tenali said, "I am so happy today. While this tree will bear fruit once a year, but I've been rewarded twice after planting this tree!"

Babur was pleased and rewarded him yet again. Then the minister interrupted. He advised Babur to move ahead so that he did not spend all his money on one person. After they had taken a few steps, Tenali yelled, "Your Majesty! Wait a minute!" When Babur turned back he said, "You did not recognise me, Your Highness! I am your humble Tenalirama." Realising that this intelligent man had duped him, Babur burst into peals of laughter. He praised Tenali's intelligence and rewarded him profusely.

02 Why the Crocodile Has a Rough Back

A long time back, crocodiles had a back as slick and smooth as a python's. One hot sultry day, a crocodile was taking his afternoon nap. Just then, a rabbit came running and tumbled over him. The crocodile slowly opened his eyes and blinked at him. "Why did you wake me up, my dear rabbit?" he asked. "Oh! Don't ask me. A man has set a dog behind me. His name is Trouble. I have had a lot of bother from Trouble since morning. Trouble can never bother me," boasted the crocodile. "You should not talk like that. Trouble doesn't like to be talked about that way," said the rabbit. The crocodile's ego was hurt. He went to find Trouble and teach him a lesson. He trudged through the tall dry grass and said aloud, "Trouble, where are you? Come out." His hollering startled a flamingo and he flew up into the air. Her sudden flight scared a monkey who was enjoying his pipe. He jumped and his pipe fell on the grass below. Before the crocodile could do anything hungry flames almost trapped him. He rushed to the nearby pond to put down the flames. His back was burnt and since then it has been hard and rocky as a riverbed.

03 Three Runners

Once two masons came to a rich man's estate in search of work. One of them had a work permit and the other did not. So he could be arrested if he ever worked without the permit. While contemplating what to do, they saw a guard coming towards them and started running. The guard followed them. Finally, the guard got hold of them and asked to see their permits. The mason with the permit showed the permit first and secretly slipped it in his friend's hand who too showed the same permit. Sensing some foul play, the guard asked why were they running. The masons very wittily replied that they were asked by their doctor to run a mile every day to reduce weight. "Oh, really! Then why didn't you stop when you saw I was chasing you?" bawled the guard. "I was stupid. Actually, I thought your doctor too has advised you to run."

04 New Shoes

A man once decided to buy a pair of new shoes. Before going to the market, he decided to take perfect measurements of his feet so that his shoes fit him fine. He put his feet on a sheet of paper, drew a detailed picture of them and even took down all the measurements in detail. Then he set off for the market. When he arrived at the shoe store, much to his disgust, he discovered that he had forgotten to bring the sheet of paper. "How shall I buy my shoes now?" thought he and went back to fetch it. When he returned to the market, it was well past evening. Most of the shops were closed. He noticed that there was a shop still open. The shopkeeper was packing all his wares. He explained his situation to him. The shopkeeper was dumbfounded. "When you are here, what is the need for all these diagrams and measurements of your feet?" he said in astonishment.

05 Anansi and the Phantom Food

Once there was a drought. Anansi the spider was very unhappy. All his people were starving. He left his village to find food for his people and himself. He walked many miles, until at last he saw smoke from a distant village. When he reached there, the only food he found was cassava. One cassava asked Anansi, "Would you like us roasted, fried or boiled?" Anansi told them he had no particular choice, so they roasted themselves. He was just about to eat them, when he noticed smoke at a distance. He came to know from the cassavas that the smoke was from the town of rice. "Rice is much better food. Who wants to eat roasted cassava?" Saying this he went towards the town of rice. When he reached, he again noticed smoke at a distance. Anansi now turned greedy. He left the rice village and went towards the smoke hoping he would get something better than rice. But alas! When he reached there he found it was his own village. And he had no food for his villagers or himself. His greed had led him nowhere.

06 A Flock of Birds

Once, in the foothills of the Himalayas, in a dense forest, there nested a flock of wild geese on a leafy tall tree. A creeper was growing at the foot of the tree. A wise goose noticed the small creeper. "We may get into trouble because of this in future," he said. But no one paid him any heed. As time passed, the creeper grew taller and stronger. One day, a hunter came into the forest. He climbed up the tree with the help of the creeper and laid his net there. He trapped the geese in the net, much to their shock. Then, the wise goose said, "In this hour of crisis we should together give our best to rescue ourselves. Let's flap our wings together with all our force." They all flapped their wings and flew off taking the net with him. Then they came down on a tree. The net snagged in the branches and the birds flew from under it to freedom. The hunter exclaimed, "When they cooperate among themselves I can never catch them."

07 Half Educated

One day, a wolf told a jackal to address him 'sir' since the wolf was more educated. Suddenly, a tiger leapt out of a bush and asked them what they were doing, intending to pounce on them. The jackal promptly said, "No, sir. Actually, a dispute has arisen between us and only you can solve this." The tiger pleased at being called 'sir', wanted to know what the dispute was. The jackal said, "I have caught two chickens. My friend demands to have one of them since he is more educated." The tiger asked the wolf, "How educated are you?" Being scared, the wolf could hardly reply. So the jackal said that the wolf claimed to have as many degrees as his teeth. At this, the tiger opened his mouth and showing his teeth said that he was far more educated and deserves both the chicken. The clever jackal at once gave the two chickens to the tiger and ran away with the wolf.

08 Hero Jack

Shy Jack planned to visit his in-laws with his friend, Ralph. In his in-laws house, Ralph was chatting away but Jack kept mum. Ralph guzzled the delicious food that was served, while Jack had only a little. But at night, he felt hungry. He shook Ralph from his slumber and together raided the kitchen. Just as Jack was having a spoonful of pudding, his in-laws woke up. Jack quickly hid in a room where cotton was stocked. His father-in-law, thinking that there was a thief, entered the room, with a bat. However, as soon as he raised his bat, Jack with cotton all over him, started screaming. Considering him to be a ghost, the poor man fainted at once. Ralph asked everyone to close their eyes while he would chant something to drive away the apparition. While they did so, Jack rushed outside. When he reappeared, Ralph said grinning, "So you chased down the ghost." Hot tea and savouries were then served. Hero Jack this time gorged on his food.

09 The Chief's Feast

Once a chief sent out his messengers to everyone to inform them about his gala feast and also ask them to bring one calabash of palm wine with them. One of his guests was delighted to receive the invitation. But he had no intention to carry palm wine with him. He thought to himself, "What harm a calabash of water can do when hundreds of people would pour down their palm wine into the chief's pot." Slowly, the much-awaited day arrived. Everyone dressed in their best fineries reached the chief's house. As each of them entered, they poured down the content of their calabash into chieftain's pot. When all guests arrived, the chief ordered his servants to fill everyone's cup with wine. The man was impatient to sip some sweet palm wine. When the chief gave his signal, the guests took their cups to their lips to have a sip of palm wine. But to their surprise, what they tasted was water. Actually, each guest thought that his one calabash of water wouldn't spoil a great pot of good wine and each had brought water.

10 Susan's Greed

Susan and Jack were excited. Cousin Eliza was dining with them that day. Mother made rice pudding, which Susan was particularly fond of, for the occasion. When mummy kept all the food in the larder and went to wash clothes, Susan thought the time was excellent to go and taste some of the pudding. The pudding was kept on the top most shelf. As Susan lifted the lid of the container, it toppled over her head. "Susan, Susan…" called out mummy. Susan ran out. And saw her cousin Eliza standing at the gate, gracefully dressed as always. Father and Jack were also there and they stared at Susan. Mummy was amazed and wanted to know what was dripping from Susan's head and hands. "Susan, you got to behave. And be careful about your appearance," scolded mummy pointing at Eliza. Susan realised her folly and promised never to be greedy again.

11 A Handful of Answers

A young student was going to the market to buy some vegetables for the monastery. On his way, he met a fellow student. "Where are you going, my friend?" asked the former. "Wherever my legs take me," replied the second one. Quite confused, the student discussed the reply with his teacher who advised him to ask what would his classmate would do if he had no legs. So the next day on his way he asked the second student, "I suppose you are going wherever your legs take you. But well, let me ask you…?" "Oh, no no! Today I am going where the wind takes me to," interrupted the second student. The answer confused him all the more. Later his teacher again said that he should have enquired what his classmate would do if there were no wind. But when he met the other boy the third time, before he could ask anything, the boy smiled and said that he was going to buy vegetables.

12 The Kitten Who Lost His Purr

Sooty, a little kitten had lost his purr. "I remember it all right that I had it this morning," thought he. "I must have lost it when I chased that kitten with the bow out of my garden. It must be in the garden only." He went out and asked everyone in the garden, from the sparrow to the little ant, whether they had seen his purr anywhere. Then he went up an apple tree and reached the highest branch of all from where he could see all over the garden. No, it was of no use. The purr was not to be seen anywhere. Sooty sighed and decided to climb down. Oh no! It was so difficult to come down. Sooty's head was reeling. He stayed back there where he was. After a while a little boy came into the garden and heard a mewing. He discovered Sooty trapped on the tree and helped him to come down. Sooty was so happy that he began to purr loudly to express his thanks. "Well," he thought to himself, "my purr must have been in the apple tree."

13 Anansi and the Capful of Hot Beans

Anansi and his wife, Aso got an invitation to a party from the latter's father. They reached the party dressed in all fineries. After a while, Anansi felt hungry but it was not yet time to dine. He looked at the dinner table longingly. He was disappointed not to find hot beans, his favourite dish. Anansi could smell beans being cooked and his mouth watered. He made a plan to eat them before anyone else. He pretended to go to the bathroom but instead went to the kitchen. He grabbed a plastic bag, put some hot beans into it and hid it under his hat. Since the beans were warm on his head he tried to leave early. His father-in-law being a good host chose to accompany the couple. After a while, Anansi could not bear the hot beans anymore on his head. He lifted his hat and the beans spilled out over his fancy dress and that of his father-in- law. Anansi thus disgraced himself and his wife and he developed baldness as a result of hot beans.

14 Little Friend

One day, a lion had a very bad day. Early in the morning, he chased down a rabbit but could not get hold of it! Moreover, he got a large thorn pierced in his palm and was moaning with pain. He tried very hard to pull the thorn out but failed to do so. Then he asked every animal he met for help. But none agreed to help him out. At last, the lion came to a fox. The fox said, "I can't do it myself. I'll send a little friend of mine. But for that you will have to let me kick you five times." The lion got very angry but he could help accepting the fox's terms. He decided to eat up the 'little friend' of the fox as soon as he got this thorn pulled out. The fox kicked him and went away crooning. After a while a porcupine came and quite easily pulled out the thorn. But the lion could not feel all that happy since there was no way he could eat a porcupine.

15 Birbal Identifies a Guest

Once Birbal was invited by a rich man for lunch. Though Birbal was not very fond of attending large gatherings he still went. He went to his house and many people were present there. He said to his host, "I did not know there would be so many guests." "All of them are not my guests. Except for one, they are all my employees," informed the man. "Can you identify who is the other guest," he continued with an amusing smile. "May be I could," said Birbal. "Just tell them a joke or something." The host cracked a joke as pathetic as one could be. When he finished everyone laughed uproariously. "Well," said the man, "I have told my joke. Now tell me who my guest is." Birbal identified the man correctly. The host was surprised. "How could you do it?" asked he. "Simple," said Birbal, "employees laugh at any joke cracked by their employer. When I observed that he only smirked and did not laugh at your joke I knew that he is your other guest."

16 Green Missile

In Norse mythology Balder, the god of light was the son of the chief god Odin and the goddess Frigg. Everyone loved Balder except Loki. He always wanted to harm Balder. As a preventive measure, Frigg made all the living and non-living things swear that they would never harm Balder. But Frigg missed one plant. It was mistletoe that did not swear. Loki got to know about it. He gathered one slender branch of the tree and sharpened one end of the root. He then rushed to the hall where all the gods were making merry. Some gods were having fun hurling weapons at Balder knowing very well that nothing could harm Balder. Loki went up to the blind god Hoder, who also was the brother of Balder. He was missing out on fun of jokingly hurling weapons at Balder. "You too, will have this fun. I'll guide you," said Loki as he handed over the mistletoe to Hoder. When Hoder threw it, it pierced Balder's chest and he died. Other gods captured Loki and chained him to rocks in a deep cavern. Till now he stays there awaiting his release.

17 Why the Marmot Doesn't Have a Thumb

Once upon a time, there were seven suns in the sky. One particular year they glowed so brightly that the earth faced a terrible drought. The soil cracked, the rivers dried up and the trees and the plants withered. During the period, there lived a highly skilled archer Erkhii Mergen. People went up to him and requested him to shoot the seven suns in the sky. The archer agreed and swore to himself, "If I can't shoot seven suns, I will cut my thumb and no longer be a man. I will be a marmot and live in the dark hole underneath the earth." Saying so, he shot six suns one after the other. As he was taking aim at the seventh sun, a swallow came flying and concealed the sun. When the arrow left the bow it wheezed off to hit the swallow. Thus, the seventh sun was spared. Erkhii kept his words. He cut off his thumb and went on to live as a marmot underneath the earth with four fingers in his paws.

18 Who is Honest?

Once a big debate broke out in the court of Maharaja Krishnadevaraya on who was more honest, a rich man or a poor man. The royal priest opined that the rich is always honest. Tenalirama disagreed and promised to prove his point. He took some gold coins from the royal treasury and put them into two small bags.

One bag was placed on the way of a richman and the other on a poor man's way. When the richman found the bag of gold coins, he took it thinking it to be a blessing from God. But when the poor man found the bag of gold coins, he took it to the treasury thinking that those might be a lifetime saving of someone. Tenalirama then said to the king, "Your Majesty! I think you have got the answer. Honesty does not come with richness or poverty. It varies from person to person."

19 The Magic of the Map

Once there lived a lazy young man named Henry. One day, he went out on a leisurely stroll, when he found a map of a treasure hunt lying on the street. He was all very excited and dreamt of becoming a rich man. He did not share the secret with anybody, not even his brother. The next morning, he went to the place as directed by the map. He started digging up the soil. But all his excitement vanished when he found nothing under it. Suddenly, he heard a voice. "You didn't notice the two conditions needed for finding the treasure. One has to be hardworking and the other was to share the secret of the map with someone." It was the map who was saying this. It was a magical map. Henry went back home and shared the secret with his brother. Then he concentrated on farming and gradually started loving the work from dawn to dusk. Three years later, Henry became a rich man. He did not feel like hunting for the treasure any more. He realised that he now held the key to all the treasures in life through hard work.

20 Birbal's Choice

One day, Emperor Akbar was holding his court when he asked his favourite courtier, Birbal a tricky question. "If you are given a choice between justice and gold coins, what would you choose?" "Your Majesty! I would choose gold coins," replied Birbal in a clear voice. The whole court was shocked to hear his reply. Some courtiers always wanted to disgrace Birbal in the emperor's eyes, but they never got a chance and now Birbal had done it himself! They knew not how to react. The most shocked person was definitely the emperor. He almost screamed, "Birbal! How could you say this! I never knew you are so greedy by nature." But Birbal was smiling. With a calm face he said, "My Lord! I am sorry to have disappointed you. But a man should ask for something that he does not possess. You have made it sure that justice belongs to everyone in this country. I already have justice. That's why I chose gold coins. You really do magic with your words, Birbal," The emperor burst into laughter and rewarded Birbal with thousand gold coins for his intelligent reply.

21 Coconut Tree's Origin

King Trishanku had a strong desire to visit Heaven in flesh and blood. Sage Vishwamitra promised to help him to fulfill his dream. So Vishwamitra performed a rite and King Trishanku began to rise towards Heaven. But Indra, the king of gods was not at all pleased with a mortal's ascent to Heaven. When the latter reached the gates of Heaven, Indra cursed him and Trishanku started falling down. Standing on Earth, Vishwamitra saw Trishanku hurtling down and cried, "Let Trishanku stay where he is now." Just as he uttered, Trishanku's fall was arrested and he remained suspended between Heaven and Earth. To make Trishanku stay where he was, Vishwamitra propped him up with a pole which eventually turned into a coconut tree and Trishanku's head became its fruit. The fibre around the coconut is his beard. So, when one takes it off, he can see Trishanku's eyes staring at him.

22 The Honest Woodcutter

One day, a poor woodcutter was cutting wood on the bank of a river. Accidentally, his axe fell into the river. He burst into tears thinking he had lost it forever and now, he and his family would starve to death. He was so poor that he would not afford to buy another one now. The river god heard his wailing and took pity on this distressed man. He appeared in front of the man and asked, "Don't cry my dear. I have heard your problem. You'll get back your axe." Saying this the god presented a gold axe in front of him. "This is not my axe, my lord," said the woodcutter. The god dipped into the water and brought a silver axe with him. "This axe is also not mine," said the woodcutter again. The god again dipped into the water and this time he brought the right axe. The face of the woodcutter beamed with joy. Now, he and his family would not have to starve. The god then gave him the gold and silver axes and said, "I admire your honesty. Take these two as rewards."

23 Battle of Wits

One day, Badwit hatched a plan to outwit Goodwit. He plucked a mango and wrapped it well with a piece of cloth. When Goodwit arrived at his house, Badwit asked Goodwit to guess what fruit was it, saying that if Goodwit fails, he would carry one thing out of Goodwit's house and if

Goodwit wins, he too could do the same. But Goodwit's guesses were all wrong. So Badwit appeared at Goodwit's house and spotted a metal chest on the rooftop, which he knew had all the money and ornaments of the house. "Oh ho! You should have hidden it from my eyes," said Badwit with a mock sympathy and brought out a ladder from the house to climb up. Seeing him, Goodwit thanked him saying, "Thanks for sparing my valuables and carrying out only the ladder."

24 Hyena and His Slaves

A hyena had two slaves, a dog and a ram. The hyena was lazy and planned to eat one of his slaves one day. But before that, he wanted them to be well fed. So he roamed around in the forest with them and reached a place where some men were eating honey. The ram collected some honey and put it on a little gourd that he was carrying. The dog found a sandal lying and took it away stealthily to eat. Suddenly, their master attacked them. But both managed to flee away. Still the danger was not yet over as they almost rammed into a lion. As the lion paused to jump at them, they dipped the shoe into the honey and gave it to him. The lion ate it and loved the honey all too much. He demanded for more. "It's not with us. It is in the hyena's stomach," said the dog. As the lion went to deal with the hyena they fled away.

25 The Lad and the Fox

Once upon a time there was a little boy who always dreamt high about himself. One day, on his way to church he saw a fox lying on a big stone fast asleep. The boy instantly started day dreaming. "If I kill the fox and sell its skin I'll earn a lot of money. Then I'll buy some rye and sow them in my father's cornfield. When people will pass by my rye field they will envy me for having such a rye field and will say, 'Oh! Wish we could have such a splendid rye field.' But I won't like their presence. I'll scream at them, 'Keep away from my rye!' But they won't listen to me. I'll again scream, 'Hey! Keep away from my rye!'" Again, they won't pay any heed to me. Then I will scream with all my might 'Keep away from my rye!' This time the boy screamed so loud that it awakened the fox from its slumber and it fled away deep into the jungle. So, the boy screamed about the undone deeds without doing the thing that should be done first and as a result lost everything.

26 A Hundred Faces

Once, a king asked a peasant about his welfare. The man informed that he earned four coins a day. "I spend one coin on myself, one I give in gratitude, one I give back and one I give on interest." Then the man explained that a part of the money he spent on himself, one part for his wife in gratitude, another part for the parents and the last part for his children that they would pay him pack with interest by taking good care of him and his wife. The king was thrilled to have found an interesting riddle. "It's wonderful! Please keep the answer secret for sometime now until you see my hundred faces," said the king. In the court, the king asked everyone the answer of the riddle. No one gave the right answer. But on the following morning one courtier came up with the right answer. The king understood that the peasant had not kept his promise and sent for him. "But, Your Majesty! I kept my promise. Before I divulged the answer the man gave me a hundred coins and all of them had your face," explained the peasant.

27 Birbal Returns Home

Once Birbal went to Persia on an invitation from the king of the land. There he was greeted with a lot of respect and warmth. On the eve of his return, one noble man asked him, "How do you compare your monarch with ours?" "Your monarch is like a full moon whereas our monarch can be likened to a quarter moon," replied Birbal. The Persians were very happy with his comment. But when his answer reached the ears of Emperor Akbar too, he was visibly not at all impressed. "You belittled me, you traitor," growled the emperor. "No, Your Majesty! You have all got me wrong. How can I belittle you?" said Birbal in a calm voice. "The full moon diminishes and finally disappears whereas the quarter moon goes strength to strength. What I actually meant is that, your power is growing day by day and the king of Persia is on the way of decline." "Oh Birbal! You and your words! Really…" the king breathed a sigh of relief and embraced Birbal warmly.

28 One Little Inch

Once upon a time a boy, as small as just an inch, was born to a couple. They named him Issun Boshi meaning, 'Little one inch.' When Issun Boshi became fifteen, he set out to see the world. In Kyoto, he got employed in the house of a wealthy merchant. His sincerity earned him the love of his master and his daughter found a wonderful companion in him. One day, these two young people were going to the temple when two giants appeared in front of them. One giant picked him up and swallowed him. Now, Issun Boshi had a needle which he wore like a sword around his waist. Within the stomach he took out his needle and rammed into the giant's throat and stabbed it so hard that the giant had to spit him out. When the other giant bent down to look at him he hit his eyes. Frightened, both the giants fled away leaving a magic mallet behind. Issun Boshi touched it and became a normal young man. The merchant gave away his daughter's hand in marriage to him and they lived happily ever after.

29 Alms

One day, a beggar was sitting at the roadside when a kingly man came near him in a chariot. The beggar beamed in joy with the hope of getting good alms. But before he could ask for anything, the man held out his hand and said, "Give me some alms." The beggar was dumfounded. Reluctantly, he gave the man the smallest grain he had. The man took it, smiled and went away. In the evening, when the beggar returned home, he poured out the contents of his bag and he was stunned to see a small grain of gold among other things. He realised that god had come to him in disguise. In remorse, he burst into tears and cried, "Why couldn't I offer him everything and get all his love."

30 King of Birds

Once all the birds of the world assembled together to decide upon their leader. After many arguments, it was decided that the leader would be chosen through a competition. During sunset the birds were supposed to fly up in the sky and touch the hand of god. The first one to reach there would be the leader. Owl, Eagle and Kori Bustard were the prominent competitors. But during the competition a tiny warbler hid itself in the Eagle's feathers and when the Eagle was about to touch heaven the warbler went ahead and touched it. All the birds became angry with him for this trickery and refused to accept him as the leader. Till this day they are arguing over who should be their leader.

31 Birbal Betrays Himself

Once Emperor Akbar and Raja Birbal had a terrible fight. Emperor Akbar called Birbal a fool and said, "Your wit and intelligence is a mere show, Birbal." At this, Birbal took offence and stormed out of the palace swearing never to return again. Now, Akbar missed Birbal and wanted him back. So he made a plan to know Birbal's whereabouts. He declared to give a thousand gold coins to any man who could walk into the palace without an umbrella but had to be in the shade at the same time. People from far and wide came up with different ideas but none could satisfy the king's condition. One day, a villager came into the palace carrying a coir cot over his head. He walked in the sun without an umbrella but at the same time was under the shade of the cot. "Bravo! You are indeed an intelligent man. Here is your thousand gold coins, clever man," said Akbar quite pleased. He then asked the man if he knew Birbal. After much interrogation, the villager divulged that it was Birbal's idea and he was staying with him. Hearing him, Emperor Akbar at once stood up and ordered for his horse. Accompanied by the villager, he himself went to meet Birbal and said, "Birbal I was wrong in saying so. You're indeed a wise man. Do come back... ." Birbal agreed and both had a happy reunion.

Contents

The Story of the Month: Hans in Luck

The Story of the Month

Hans in Luck

November

01 Hans in Luck

Hans was a faithful servant of a rich merchant. He served his master well for many years and finally decided to go back to his mother in the village. His master gave him a huge gold slab as a reward for his service. On his way, Hans met a man riding a handsome horse. "Can I exchange my gold for your horse," asked Hans. The man readily agreed and Hans rode on his horse singing merrily. "Hip! Hip!" said Hans and the horse started galloping so fast that Hans lost his balance and fell off the horse. A farmer who was passing by with his cow saved Hans and said, "Be careful boy, riding a horse needs skill." Hans exchanged his horse for the farmer's cow. But as soon as Hans tried milking the cow, it kicked Hans and knocked him unconscious. Hans regained his senses and exchanged the cow with a farmer's pig. Happy that he could get rid of the useless cow, Hans continued his journey carrying the pig along with him. As he was walking by the meadows, he saw a young man carrying a beautiful goose under his arm. "Wow! I wish I could have that," thought Hans and walked up to the young man and complimented his goose. To his surprise, the young man said, "Would you like to have it? Actually I fear to take your pig because the mayor's pig is missing since morning. I wonder if this could be the one." Scared at being caught, Hans requested the young man to take his pig and give him the goose. After much pleading, the young man agreed and gave Hans the goose saying, "It will make a delicious roast. Go home fast and relish it." Hans gladly took the goose and hurried to his village thinking to give his mother a pleasant surprise with the goose. As he neared his village, he came across a knife-grinder. Quite impressed with the

knife-grinder's work, he went up to the knife-grinder and praised his work. "Young man, you too can become a knife-grinder and earn good money. All you need is a whetstone," said the knife-grinder. Saying so, the knife-grinder offered to give Hans his damaged whetstone in exchange for the goose. Hans at once agreed and taking the whetstone along with another stone from the knife-grinder, resumed his journey home. After a while, he felt tired carrying the heavy stones and sat down near a pond under the shade of a tree. Plop! Fell the stones into the pond as Hans rested his head on them to lie down. Happy that he had managed to get rid of the heavy stones. Hans walked home happily to meet his mother.

02 The Dress

Margaret insisted on wearing her cousin, Mary's new blue silk dress for her birthday. "I'll wear Mary's blue dress on my birthday," she announced. Now, Mary had to wear the blue dress for a special occasion too. "What shall I do?" thought Mary for she knew how stubborn her cousin was. So on Margaret's birthday, Mary went along with Margaret's parents to wish her in the morning. "Happy birthday, Margaret," wished all. "Wear this for the evening party," said Mary handing her blue dress to Margaret. "Errr… thank you…" Margaret couldn't believe her eyes. Her parents then showed her two tickets to the newest fun spot in town. Margaret was thrilled but to her dismay her mother handed the tickets to Mary saying that she deserved since she gave Margaret her dress to wear. Margaret thought for a moment and her mistake. She returned Mary's dress and taking the tickets from her mother, rushed to get ready to go to the fun spot with Mary.

03 Anansi and the Turtle

Anansi, the spider, once baked some delicious yams. Knock! Knock! Anansi heard someone knocking at the door. It was Turtle. "Can I share your meal?" asked Turtle. As was customary in his country, Anansi couldn't refuse a meal to his guest and invited Turtle, though reluctantly. But as soon as Turtle sat down to eat, Anansi asked him to wash his hands and sent him to the river. When Turtle returned, he found Anansi already eating. As he sat down to have his meal, Anansi again pointed at his dirty hands. But by the time Turtle returned from his second wash, Anansi ate up all the yams. Turtle then invited Anansi to his house at the river bed and left. When Anansi went to Turtle's house, he filled his pockets with stones to avoid floating on the surface. At the dining table Turtle asked Anansi to remove his jacket before eating. But as soon as he did so, Anansi floated to the surface and was thus deprived of a delicious lunch.

04   The Dirty Pig

One day, a young pig was drinking water from a lake. Suddenly, he saw the reflection of a lion in the water. The pig turned around. "Grrr..." growled the lion and stepped back. Seeing this, the pig thought that the lion feared him and challenged the lion for a fight. The lion refused saying that they would fight the next day. Thinking that he was superior to the lion, the pig went home and boasted, "I'll soon be the king of the forest. Even the lion fears my strength." Hearing him Grandpa Pig said, "It's not your strength but your body odor that made the lion move away. So tomorrow roll yourself in the mud and be as dirty as possible, else the lion will kill you". "So the next morning, the pig rolled himself in the mud and elephant dung and became as dirty as he could. When he met the lion, the foul smell made the lion feel nauseated and he lost his appetite. "Go away, you dirty fellow," roared the lion and the pig ran away.

05   The Bachelors and the Python

In a village in Africa there lived two bachelors, Niger and Neil. While Niger was kind and gentle, Neil was haughty and rude. They lead very lonely lives. One day, Niger went out with his bow and arrow to hunt in the forest. He hunted two wild cats—one black and the other brown. While he was returning home with his games, he met Mozo, the great rock python. "I'm stiff with cold. Please do carry me to the warm river," pleaded Mozo. Kind Niger carried Mozo on his shoulder and threw him into the river. Mozo then instructed Niger to throw his hunts in the river and take what the river god gave him. And lo, a beautiful maiden came out of a gourd. Niger lived happily with his wife. Soon, Neil came to know how Niger got his wife and decided to have a wife in the same way. But Neil refused to help Mozo go to the cold river and got nothing in return.

06 The Boatman

A scholar once had to cross a river. "Can you ferry me across," asked the scholar to a boatman waiting at the shore. "Sure, sir" said the boatman and asked the scholar to get into his boat. Intending to start a conversation, the scholar asked the boatman, "Do you know any rules of grammar or phonetics?" asked the scholar to the boatman. The boatman thought for a while and said, "No, I don't know. In fact I had never learnt grammar rules in my life. Oh! What a pity! You've wasted half of your life then," said the scholar wearing a sympathetic look. The boatman kept quiet and continued to row the oars. Suddenly the rickety boat stopped with a jerk as it hit against a huge rock. "Bang!" came a sound and the boat started sinking. The boatman turned around and asked the scholar if he had learnt to swim. When the scholar said that he didn't know how to swim, the boatman smiled and said, "You've wasted all your life as you'll be drowned soon."

07 The Old Couple Who Made the Trees Blossom

An old couple had a little dog called Snifer and took good care of him. But their neighbour was a mean old man who hated dogs and pelted stones at Snifer. One day, Snifer helped his master get a pot of gold coins from the courtyard. Seeing this, the mean neighbour borrowed Snifer and asked the dog to do the same. When Snifer couldn't, he killed the dog in a fit of rage. The old couple buried Snifer in the courtyard and planted a pine tree over his grave. They made a mortar with the pinewood to make rice cakes in Snifer's memory. But the moment they put in the wet rice to grind, it turned into gold. Once again the neighbour tried his luck with the mortar and burnt it to ashes when he got garbage instead of gold. Sadly, the old couple got the ashes and sprinkled on the cherry trees which blossomed overnight. They even helped the prince to revive his favourite cherry tree with the mortar's ashes who rewarded the old couple handsomely.

08 The Rabbit Steals the Elephant's Dinner

Jerry was a mischievous, lazy rabbit. "I can make a noose of creepers and use it as a trap. It'll be great fun to see the animals hanging in mid air", thought Jerry. Quite disturbed with Jerry's trick, Polo, the elephant called a meeting to find out who laid the noose trap. All came except Jerry, who was busy stealing Polo's beans. When Polo returned and found the beans missing, he asked Leo the lion to keep a watch and catch the thief. Jerry heard the plan and next morning, he laid the noose near the cooking pots. Leo got trapped in the noose and hung in mid air till he was rescued by the other animals. Terry, the tortoise then volunteered to keep watch. He asked Polo's wife to sprinkle salt on him and hid among the beans. As Jerry ate the bean, he bit hard on Jerry's foot and caught him. Jerry was hung in a noose for days without food and became so weak, that the animals took pity on him and set him free.

09 Rope Trick

A villager and his family on their way to the city, rested under a Banyan tree for the night. The villager did not like idling his time. So he sent his sons to gather firewood and water and then asked his wife to knead the dough, while he made a rope. A giant lived in the Banyan tree and when he saw the villager making a rope, he came down and asked, "Why are you making that rope?" The clever villager looked at the giant and said, "I'm making the rope to tie you." "Err… please don't do that. I'll give you something if you spare me," pleaded the giant who was actually a coward at heart. Saying so, the giant brought a bag full of gold coins and gave to the villager. "Hmm… I think I should spare you for the wonderful gift you have given me," said the villager and taking the bag of gold coins, left for his village.

10 Why the Warthog Goes About on His Knees

The warthog made himself a cosy spacious home in an old termite mound. Every day, he stood at his grand entrance and savoured the feeling of owning a palatial house. One day, while the warthog was standing at his entrance, a lion came stalking at him. The warthog ran inside and looked for a place to hide. "I need to play the jackal's trick on the lion", thought the warthog and stood with his back rose, pretending to hold the roof. "Oh King of the forest, help me else the roof will fall and we'll be crushed," implored the warthog. But the lion understood the foolish warthog's trick for he remembered how the jackal fooled him and roared so loudly, that the warthog knelt down and started pleading for life. "Silly creature, I'll spare you but be on your knees," said the lion and left as he was not feeling hungry. From then on, the warthog stays on his knees with his bottom up in the air and his snout snuffling in the dust.

11 A Question of Time

One hot sunny morning, Nasruddin Hodja was tilling his field, feeling quite weary because of the heat. Suddenly, a hunter came riding up and asked, "Did you see a boar run past?" Hodja thought for a while and nodded his head, still busily tilling. "Which way did it go?" demanded the hunter, sounding a bit annoyed. Hodja lifted his head and putting down his hoe, pointed towards the north with his forefinger. Without even thanking Hodja, the hunter rode away towards the north, hoping to catch his game. Hodja resumed his tilling while the hunter went galloping further. After a while, the hunter returned looking very tired and angry. He stopped his horse near Hodja and asked, "I could see no trace of the boar. Are you sure you've seen it going towards the north?" Hodja wore a serious look and said, "Sure? I'm certain that it went that way because I had seen it going last year." The hunter wore a confused look and thinking Hodja to be out of his mind, left without uttering a word.

12 Rama, the Dutiful Son

King Krishnadevaraya failed to fulfill his mother's last wish which was to eat mangoes. Knowing this, the greedy courtiers suggested the king to give each of them a golden mango for his mother's soul to rest in peace. The king believed them and did accordingly. Tenalirama decided to teach the courtiers a lesson. He waited at the door with a red hot iron and announced, "You'll get as many golden mangoes as burnt marks you agree to have on your body." This surprised the courtiers but unable to resist the temptation of the golden mangoes, bore the burnt marks on their body. Unable to bear any further, they went and complained the king about Tenalirama. The king called Tenalirama and asked why he had done that to the courtiers. Tenalirama humbly said, "It was to fulfill my mother's last wish who died before her wish could be fulfilled." The King understood Tenalirama's intention and laughed out.

13 The Lion and the Rabbit

The animals of the forest made a deal with the lion to stop his pleasure hunt. They offered to send an animal every day to the lion as his meal. The lion agreed and from that day, an animal sacrificed his life each day to satisfy the lion's hunger. Finally, it was the turn of the rabbit. "I'll have to put an end to this practice," thought the rabbit and contrived a plan. He slowly went to the lion's den wearing a very pale look. "Why are you so late? Can't you see I'm hungry," roared the lion. "Err… I was held back by the other lion near the deep well," said the rabbit sheepishly. Hearing this, the lion became very angry and rushed to the deep well to meet his rival. The lion saw his own reflection in the water and became wild with anger. Roar… he roared aloud and jumped straight into the deep well to fight the other lion and was drowned.

14 Nasruddin Hodja and Clever Peter in the Cherry Orchard

Nasruddin Hodja and Clever Peter once went to pick cherries from a neighbour's orchard. They climbed up a tree which was full of ripe cherries. Being stronger than Clever Peter, Nasruddin Hodja climbed to the highest branch which had the reddest of cherries. "Umm… They are indeed so tasty," Hodja said relishing the sweet cherries. After a while he noticed that Clever Peter was eating only half ripe cherries. So he invited Peter to climb up and eat the red ones. But Clever Peter was scared to climb so high and refused. "Hold, I'm bending the branch for you to pluck some ripe cherries," shouted out Hodja to Clever Peter and bent the branch with ripe cherries. Clever Peter held the branch and started plucking the red cherries. Suddenly, Hodja let go off the branch and Clever Peter came flying down and fell on some thorns near a rabbit. He deftly caught the rabbit and pretended to have come down just for it.

15 The Lazy Donkeys

A merchant had some lazy donkeys who hated carrying loads. One day, the merchant loaded bags of salt on a donkey and set off for the market. On the way, they had to cross a river and the donkey slipped. The salt got dissolved in the water and the donkey's load lessened. At night, the donkey shared his experience with his friends and henceforth all the donkeys decided to purposely slip in the water to lessen their load. The next day the farmer took another donkey and went to the market, taking care not to let the donkey slip. But the donkey remembered his friends words and as soon as they were in the water, he kneeled and dipped the bags on his back in water. But alas! The bags were filled with cotton and the moment it got wet; the cotton absorbed the water and became heavy. "Hee haw… cried the poor donkey overburdened with the weight and cursed himself for his foolish act.

16 The three Brothers

A widow had three sons. She loved the eldest son the most, who was actually her stepson. The boy was hard working and the family prospered. Misled by the jealous neighbours, the younger brothers decided to get rid of the elder brother. Under her son's pressure, the widow made her eldest son believe that a snake had crept into his stomach and he lost his appetite. He became so weak that he took to his bed. The neighbours took advantage of this and encroached upon the widow's land. The two brothers failed to deal with the crisis and realising their mistake pleaded their mother to help their brother regain his health. The widow then made the eldest son believe that the snake had crept out of his stomach and there was nothing to fear. The son then regained his health and got back their land from the neighbours. Once again they all lived happily.

17 A Woman and the Bell of Miidera

The huge sparkling bronze bell in the Miidera monastery in Japan was never allowed to be touched by any woman as the priest believed that a woman's touch would not only lose its shine but a calamity would befall them. The beautiful queen heard about the bell and its charms. "I want to see my reflection on it," the queen told the king. The king loved his wife dearly and gave in to her requests. So the queen was taken to the monastery in a golden palanquin. The shine of the bell amazed her and she felt tempted to touch it. But just as she struck the bell, it became dull and a hole appeared on the surface. Before anybody could realise what had happened, a severe earthquake rocked the city and it fell into ruins.

18 The Ungrateful Friend

A woodcutter once met a blind tiger in the forest and cured the tiger's blindness with the juice of some herbs. Both became great friends and started living together. Every day, the tiger went out and hunted different animals with his renewed eyesight. He gave the major portion of his hunt to the woodcutter, who slept the whole day and fed on meat soup every night. This made the woodcutter very healthy and he looked younger. One day, the woodcutter boasted of his improved health and the tiger said jokingly, "It would be nice to eat your flesh." This scared the wood cutter and he decided to get rid of the tiger. So he dug a deep hole on the tiger's way and covered it with dry leaves. The tiger fell into it and starved to death. The wood cutter buried him in the forest and after a few days found precious jewels in the tiger's grave. Henceforth, the woodcutter became a rich man but he always repented what he had done to his friend.

19 The Jewel Thieves

Once upon a time a severe drought hit the village of Vijayanagara, where the wise courtier Tenalirama lived. The villagers began fleeing to neighbouring villages in the hope of finding some water. A group of wicked thieves decided to break into the deserted households and loot all their belongings. One night, they came near Tenalirama's house. When the wise courtier saw the men hiding behind a tree, he realised their intent. He yelled for his son, "My dear son, please keep all the precious jewels in a box and throw it down into the well. With so many people leaving this village, we can be in danger of being robbed." Tenali's son realised his father's plan and packed some heavy stones in a box and threw it into the well. At midnight the thieves jumped into the well to look for the jewels. While they were busy searching, Tenalirama called the king's soldiers and had the thieves arrested. The next day, the king congratulated Tenalirama for showing such courage and intelligence.

20 The Magic Pear Tree

A farmer once took a cart full of ripe pears to sell. "Pears for sale!" shouted out the farmer. A monk came up to him and asked for a pear. "Go away, you old brat!" the farmer chased the monk away. A man heard the monk and bought a pear for him. The monk was overjoyed and relished the pear. As he was about to finish it, the monk suddenly declared, "I invite all of you to come over and have a pear from my pear tree." Saying so, he planted the pip of the pear he was eating in the ground and to everybody's amazement a pear tree grew out of it. The crowd tasted the monk's delicious pears and was awestruck when the monk cut down the tree with his axe and carried it on his shoulder. The farmer, who was also watching, suddenly noticed that his cart was empty and one of the handles was lying at a distance on the road. He understood what the monk had done and became mad with anger.

21 Why the Bat Flies at Night

The birds and the animals were once at war with each other. Everyone, except the bat joined the war. "I will join the winners only," decided the bat and went to the birds who were winning at that point of time. "Go away, you ugly monster," shouted the peacock, who was the general of the Birds' Army. The bat flapped its wings and pleaded to join the Birds' Camp saying:

O' Friends I'm one among you
Don't consider me to be someone new
See how I fly
I'm not a creature who is sly

Hearing him, the birds allowed him to join them. But as the birds were engrossed in rejoicing their victory, the animals made a sudden attack and defeated them. So the bat went to be in the animals' team. But when they refused, the birds too chased him away. Since then, the bat comes out only at night all alone.

22 Hair Transplant

An old man was once watching a weaver weaving a blanket. While the weaver was lost in his work, the old man pulled out a few of his grey strands and mixed them with the wool the weaver was using and left. After a few days, the weaver took the blanket to the market to sell. The old man followed him and as the weaver made a deal with a customer for the blanket, the old man showed up and demanded his share. "Which share are you talking of?" asked the surprised weaver. The old man then took the blanket and showed that his hair was also woven into it along with the wool. The hermit's slyness annoyed the weaver but he could do nothing except giving him a share of the blanket's profit.

23 A Fright for Tiger

A tiger lived on the outskirts of a village. He was a man eater and the villagers were in great terror. On a tall tree just outside the village, a young boy sat guarding. Whenever he saw the tiger approaching, he beat his drums and the villagers became alarmed. This was his daily task and the boy got so tired of his mundane job that he decided to put an end to the man eater. So the boy made a clay snake at home and brought it along with him to the tree. When the tiger came prowling, the boy dropped the snake and watched from the tree top. "Grrr... growled the tiger in fear when he saw the horrifying snake with his deadly fangs and ran into the forest never to come back again. So from that day the boy became free to enjoy his life playing with his friends in the wide fields.

24 Top Answers

A village headman wanted to test the intelligence of
his only daughter-in-law and asked if she knew how
much he had spent on their wedding. "Yes, the cost
of a bag of rice," replied the daughter-in- law. This
annoyed the headman greatly. One day, while
going to a wedding, they saw a funeral procession
and the daughter-in-law enquired if it was one man's
funeral or a hundred's. Infuriated, the headman
asked what she meant. The daughter- in-law smiled
and explained how a man's dependents suffer when
he dies and if farmers are indebted, they can never
enjoy their harvest. Impressed with her answers, the
headman asked her why she had told him that he had spent
only the cost of a bag of rice on their wedding. "The actual ritual
needed only a few hundred rupees. The rest was spent on false show,"
replied the daughter-in-law and the headman burst out laughing.

25 The Shrewd Businessman

Tenalirama, the witty and intelligent minister, had to prove to
King Krishnadevaraya that the business class is more cunning
and shrewd than the brahmins. First, he went to the royal
priest and asked him to shave off his ponytail. Tenalirama
succeeded in convincing the priest to carry out the
king's order in return for five gold coins. Next, he
went to the biggest businessman in town who had
a big, thick ponytail. "My status in society depends
on my ponytail. If I shave it off, people will think
I've become a poor man," said the businessman.
He finally agreed to shave it for ten thousand gold
coins. The barber was called in to carry out the
task. But just as the barber took out his razor, the
businessman said, "This ponytail now belongs to the
king. How can you rob the king of his honour?" The
king smiled at the businessman's words and let him go. He
was convinced that the business class was certainly shrewder
than the brahmins.

26 The Honest Thief

Benny, a cunning thief planned to rob the pilgrims coming to the nearby temple. He developed friendship with a rich pilgrim and became so close that he confessed his intentions to him. On knowing his intentions, the pilgrim shared his money with Benny and advised him to always speak the truth. Since his friend had not asked him to stop stealing, Benny decided to continue stealing but with honesty. So one day, Benny went to rob the king's palace. "Who are you and what do you want?" asked the guards. "I'm a thief and have come to steal," replied Benny. The guards mistook him to be the King's guest and allowed him to enter and exit the palace without any difficulty. Benny returned from the palace a rich man, having robbed bagsof jewels. But from then on, he decided to give up stealing.

27 A Cartload of Almonds

A squirrel worked for king lion and served him well. Pleased with his service, the lion promised to give him a cartload of almonds when he retired. The squirrel was very pleased but whenever he saw the other squirrels enjoying a carefree life, playing and jumping all around, he longed to do the same. He envied the others but consoled himself saying, "Never mind, they'll envy me when I'll have a cartload of almonds. After all it's a delicacy which very few squirrels must have had." He continued to serve the lion relentlessly till he was old and it was time for him to retire. The lion held a banquet on his farewell and presented him the cartload of almonds as he had promised. The squirrel looked at the cartload of almonds and shouted in joy, "Thank you, My Lord. You've indeed made me rich." But his happiness was short-lived for he realised that the almonds were no longer of any 208 use to him since he had lost all his teeth with age.

28 The Mind Reader

Once a portly gentleman dressed in all fineries and riding a horse, approached Mulla Nasruddin. "Mulla, can you tell me the way to the palace?" asked the man leaning from his horse. "How did you know I am a Mulla?" Nasruddin was surprised. Now, this man had a habit of addressing any scholarly-looking man as 'Mulla' which was a title given to learned men and it meant 'master'. But the man did not tell him the real reason. Instead he smirked and said, "Well, I'm a mind reader, you know. Oh! Really! Then read my mind and know your way towards the palace," said Mulla wittily.

29 The Bee and the Pigeon

Once, a little bee fell into the water. A little bird sitting on a nearby tree saw it and held out a leaf to the bee. It crawled onto the leaf and was saved. Next morning, while the bird was sitting on a branch, a hunter aimed his arrow at it. The bee saw this and stung the hunter hard. This shook his hand and his arrow fell on the ground. Thus, the bird was saved.

30 The Silken Tassel

Once a wicked wizard wished to marry a girl named Silken Tassel. When she refused, the wizard forced her family to put her into a barrel and throw it into the river. Meanwhile, the wizard waited for the barrel to come to him. But before he spotted the barrel, a fisherman found it. Silken Tussle told him her sad story and the fisherman decided to teach the wizard a lesson. He once again floated the barrel with a fierce dog inside it and when the wizard opened it, the dog lunged on him and tore him to death.

Contents

The Story of the Month: The Three Scholars

The Story of the Month
The Three Scholars

01 The Three Scholars

Once there were three scholars. One day, they sat to talk about their capabilities and the prospects they have. Agreeing that they have acquired immense wisdom and mastered the art of magical powers, the three scholars decided to venture out of their teacher's ashram and show their talent to the world. Together they went to their teacher and divulged their plans. The teacher was reluctant to give them his permission. But when they insisted, the teacher at last allowed them to go saying, "But you must take my

domestic help with you. Treat him as your brother and pay heed to his advice if he gives you any," ordered the teacher. Soon, they set out on their journey. They were all brimming with hopes of success. "I wonder whether we would ever return to the ashram," said one of them. Others too supported his view. The fourth member quietly followed them carrying their luggage. After a few miles, they entered a forest area. All of them settled down rest for a while. While Guruji's domestic help was cooking some food, the three men kept themselves busy with their magical tricks. They spotted some crumbled bones dumped under a tree. "Let's make this a complete skeleton," proposed one friend. And uttering some mantras, he sprinkled some water on the bones. And lo! The bones joined together to form a skeleton of a huge tiger. Now, everyone was very excited. The second friend said, "See, what I can do with it. I will give it flesh and blood." The fourth person was aghast to see them playing a dangerous game. "Don't do this, you fools! You're inviting trouble," he yelled at them. But no one listened to him. The second friend too uttered some words and sprinkled some water on the skeleton. Soon, it became a carcass of a tiger. "Want to see what I can do?" said the third friend feeling all eager. "I can breathe life into it. Oh, yes! The tiger will always be so grateful to us," encouraged the other two. The fourth person screamed, "Have you gone crazy? The tiger will eat you up." But in vain he shouted. No one cared to listen to him. Before the third friend sprinkled water on the carcass, the man quickly climbed up the tree. As soon as the third scholar sprinkled water the tiger woke up with a terrifying roar. It stirred his body, stretched its limbs and yawned so big that it seemed he had woken up from a hundred years of sleep. It looked around and saw its meal ready in front of it. With another loud roar, the tiger jumped on the three of them. The wise man returned home with a broken heart and informed the teacher about their unfortunate death.

02 Why the Sun and the Moon Live in the Sky

A long, long time back, the Sun and the Water were close friends and lived together on Earth. The Sun used to visit Water quite often but the Water never paid him any visit. One day, the Sun asked the Water, "My dear friend, why don't you visit my house? If I go to your place then I'll have to take all my people with me. I don't think your house is big enough to fill all of us," replied the Water. The Sun said that would not be a problem and asked him to come. Next day, the Water appeared at the Sun's place and began to flow in with fish and sea animals. When the Water was knee deep, he asked whether it was still safe to enter. The Sun and his wife said, "Yes," and so more of them flowed till the Sun and the moon had to sit at the top of the house. They did not ask the Water to stop and the Water flowed over the roof top. The Sun and the moon were forced to go up in the sky and since then they live there.

03 Why Snakes Have Forked Tongues

Kadru and Vinata, the wives of King Kashyap hated each other. Once they betted over the colour of Uchchaisravas, the horse produced just after the time of creation. Vinata lost the bet and as per the agreement, was imprisoned by Kadru's serpent sons. The snakes were ready to release her only if Vinata's son Garuda, the half-human, half eagle king of birds would bring them amrita (the nectar of immortality). Garuda fetched the nectar and the snakes released his mother. But before they could drink their desired ambrosia, Indra, the king of gods recovered the pot. The snakes tried desperately to lick the drops of nectar that had fallen on the ground where the pot was kept and the sharp blades of the grass slit their tongues. Since then, the tongues of all snakes are forked.

04 The Story of Bausis and Philemon

Once Zeus, the king of Mount Olympus, came down to Earth in the disguise of a beggar. Everyone turned him away until he came to the house of a poor elderly couple, Bausis and Philemon. They welcomed him warmly and offered him some bread and wine to eat. The beggar sat down with them to eat. Surprisingly, the wine jug never emptied and there were always more bread after each slice was cut. Bausis and his wife were stunned and they realised that the guest was no ordinary beggar. Then Zeus came back to his form and said, "I am very pleased with your generosity. You gave away the best you had. Wish for anything and it will be granted." The couple had only one wish to remain together for ever. It so happened that when Bausis and Philemon died, an oak and a linden tree grew with their trunks entwined around each other on the very spot where they were buried.

05 The Fairy Tulips

Once there lived an old woman who had a beautiful bed of striped tulips in her garden. One night, her sleep was suddenly broken by soft sounds of sweet singing and gurgles of babies' laughter. She woke up and went out to find a little fairy mother crooning and rocking the flower like a cradle, while in each tulip-cup lay a little fairy baby laughing and playing. The old woman quietly came back home and since then, she never let anyone touch and the pluck the flowers. The tulip grew bigger and brighter day by day and their sweet fragrance spread all around. One day, the woman died and her neighbours tore away the tulips and planted parsleys. But they withered and so did all the flowers in the garden. But beautiful tulips, daffodils and violets draped the woman's grave.

06 The Emperor's Servant

One day, Emperor Akbar and Raja Birbal were riding together through the country side. On their way, they passed by a cabbage field. "Look Birbal! There're so many cabbages. I love cabbages. They are simply delicious," exclaimed the emperor. "Yes, the cabbage is the king of the vegetables!" said Birbal. A few days later, both the emperor and Birbal were riding by the same patch of cabbages. But this time the emperor was not happy. "Oh! These cabbages, I hate them now. I used to love them once. But now I don't have any taste for them," said Akbar. "Yes, Your Majesty! The cabbages are the most tasteless vegetables I have ever tasted in my life," said Birbal. "But Birbal, last time we came here you said they are the king of vegetables!" The emperor was astonished. "Yes, I did," admitted Birbal. "But Your Majesty, I am your servant and not that of these cabbages," said Birbal grinning and both of them burst into laughter.

07 Prince Charming

Once there lived a handsome young king who was always very proud of his looks. One day, God came to his court and said, "I have come here to see whether you are really as handsome as you claim. I came here last night too and I found you more handsome then." Quite confused, the king asked his courtiers if what God said was true. They replied that he looked just the same. "I can identify differences that your courtiers can't with their mortal eyes. Bring a bowl of water. I'll prove it," said God. God then asked all the courtiers to study the water closely. Then they were asked to leave. God then removed a spoonful of water away from the bowl and called in the courtiers back. They were asked to identify the change but they couldn't. The king then realised his beauty was short-lived and that he had been wasting his time on everything. He renounced his crown and became a monk.

08 The Monkey's Fiddle

Once Monkey received a bow, an arrow and a fiddle which could make anyone dance to its tune from his uncle Orang Outang. On his way, he helped Brer Wolf to kill a deer with his bow and arrow. Seeing this, Brer Wolf decided to have the bow and arrow. A fight broke between them and they took the matter to King Lion's court. Monkey could not prove his claim over the bow and arrow. Lion declared that Monkey was guilty and he was asked to leave the land. But Monkey still had his fiddle. He started playing it. As soon as he played the first note, everyone started to sway with the music and with increasing notes they hopped, jived and twirled till they were losing their breath. Wolf screamed, "Monkey, please stop! Then acknowledge that the bow and arrow are actually mine," yelled Monkey. "I acknowledge, I acknowledge," screamed back Wolf and Lion. Monkey got his belongings back and went back home happily.

09 Price of a Moustache

Once in the court of Raja Krishna Chandra, Gopal the court jester stated that the businessmen were cleverer than the scholars and promised to prove his statement. A few days later, Gopal called a scholar into the palace and said that the king wanted his moustache and was ready to give a good price for it. The scholar was delighted and asked for twenty gold coins. After he received the money, the barber came and shaved off his moustache. Next, he called a businessman and Gopal told him the same thing. The businessman demanded twenty thousand gold coins. He got it from the treasury but when the barber approached him, he refused to have his moustache shaved saying that it now belonged to the king and he would not let anyone touch his moustache. Raja Krishna Chandra, who had been listening from behind a screen had to agree with Gopal.

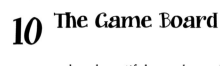

10 The Game Board

One day, a man made a beautiful wooden gebeta board, a traditional African board game, for his son. In the morning when he went with his cattle, he carried it with him. On the way, he met wandering Somalis gathered around a ring fire. "Where can we get some good wood, my dear boy," asked one of them. "Here is some," said the boy and gave them the gebeta board. As they put it into the flames, the boy began to cry. The Somalis gave him a nice knife to make him quiet. Again while walking he met a man trying to dig the ground. The man borrowed the knife but while digging, broke it. "Give me back my knife," the boy wailed. The man gave him an axe instead of the knife and the boy went away happily. On the way, a woodcutter took it and gave him a limb of a tree. When the boy was returning back, a woman took his limb to make fire and gave him a gebeta. As he entered his house his father smiled and said: "There's nothing better than a gebeta game board to keep a small boy out of trouble."

11 The Foolish Donkey

An idol maker once took an idol on his donkey's back to deliver it to a customer. The idol was one of the best specimens of his excellent craftsmanship and drew the attention of the passersby. Everyone who passed them, bowed down in front of the idol and prayed. Foolish as he was, the donkey thought they were bowing down at him. He wished not to move from a place where people regarded him with so much respect and stopped walking. His master tried all means to make him move, but he refused to budge. The more his master tried, the more he started acting pricey until the master lifted the idol on his own head and resumed his journey. The donkey remained where he was until he realised that people were no more bowing to him. Instead the crowd was now following the man and they were bowing to the idol. Ashamed at his foolishness, the donkey ran to join his master.

12 No Radish No Recipe

One day, Tenalirama had a sumptuous lunch at his friend's house and greatly appreciated the sweet dish made of radish. "Sweet dish of radish! Are you out of your wits! Who has ever heard anything like this?" said his wife disbelievingly. She simply could not picture the recipe in her mind–a sweet dish with radish! Yet, she thought of trying her hand at this new recipe. So, next morning when Tenali was going out, his wife repeatedly told him to buy some radish and get the recipe written from his friend. "Where are the radishes?" inquired his wife when he returned. "You see," explained Tenalirama, "a goat snatched the packet away while I was coming back." His wife got very annoyed at his carelessness. "Now where is the recipe, may I know?" she demanded. "Well, you know, I thought," said Tenali forcing a smile, "the recipe is of no use without the radish, so I let the animal eat that too."

13 Hairy Tale

One day, Emperor Akbar asked his courtiers why he did not have hair on his palms. Birbal came forward and said, "Your Majesty! The generous number of gifts with which you bless us constantly slip from your hands into the hands of the undeserved souls like us. This wears away every single hair that might grow in your palm." Akbar then asked, "What about your hairless palm, Birbal?" Birbal held out his hand and said, "Your Majesty! Hair grows but the constant flow of your generous gifts wear away every last hair that had grown. What about others? Nobody has hair on their palms," Akbar pointed at all others in the court. Birbal smiled and replied, "Your highness! They envy my luck and wring their palms in jealousy." The emperor burst into a loud laughter.

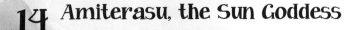

14 Amiterasu, the Sun Goddess

A long time back, Izanami, the mother of all and Izanagi, the father of all, had a beautiful little girl named Amaterasu Omikami. Little Amiterasu would climb up the sky every day and filled the earth with all her radiance. Amiterasu had a younger brother named Susanowo. He had a fierce nature and ruled the mighty oceans. He brought so much destruction on Earth that his father striped him off all the power. He then took shelter under his sister in heaven. But there too, he did not mend his ways and he destroyed all the peace of heaven. Little Amiterasu was frightened of her brother and hid herself in a cave and pulled a huge boulder to block the entrance. In a moment, there was darkness all around. Then the gods made a plan to bring her out. They gathered in front of the cave and started making merry. In the cave, Amiterasu felt curious. She opened the cave a little to see what they were cheering about. Just then, God Tajikarawo gently took hold of Amaterasu's arm and drew her out and soon, there was brightness all over.

15 Mullah Goes to a Tailor

One day, Mullah Nasruddin went to a tailor with a piece of cloth to get it stitched to a shirt. The tailor promised to get it ready in a week's time. All through the week, Mullah waited eagerly to don the new shirt. But when he visited the tailor on the seventh day, he was bitterly disappointed to know that it was not yet ready. "God willing you'll get it ready the day after tomorrow," said the man. Two days later, Mullah went again. It was not yet ready but the tailor was ready with his reply, "God willing it'll be ready on Saturday." Now, Mullah was not sure whether he would get the shirt on Saturday or whether he would get it at all. On Saturday, Mullah was again at the tailor's shop. It was the same story as he expected. "God will…," began the tailor. "No! No! Stop Stop!" interrupted Mullah, now completely fed up, "just tell me, how long will it take if you leave God out of this?"

16 A Tree of Bread

One day, a farmer discovered a brass pot filled with gold coins in the field. He hid it in their compound and asked his wife never to say anything to anyone. The wife agreed but he was not convinced, since she had a habit of blurting out everything at the slightest temptation. So he made a plan. That night when his wife slept off, he took some bread and put it on a tree near his house. The next morning his wife noticed the bread on the tree. The farmer read the astonishment on her face and said, "This tree gives bread as fruits every fifth year. Next day, the king sent for them. When they reached, the king demanded the pot of coins and insisted that since the information came from his wife to someone, it should be correct. The farmer said, "Don't believe her words. She is insane. I am not insane! We got the pot the day before the tree bore bread on it," protested the woman. The king now was fully convinced that she was insane and thus spared the farmer and his wife.

17 The Water Drop

Once there lived a little boy by the side of a stream. One day, while he was sitting by the streamside, suddenly a tiny water drop came up to him and said, "Hey! Will you be my friend?" Perplexed, the boy asked, "Why? Don't you have any other?" The water drop heaved a sigh and narrated her tale how she lived with her sisters in the ocean. But being proud, she thought she would look better with the stars and clung to the sunbeam to go up in the sky. But midway, she fell on a dark cloud. When this dark cloud laid itself on the mountain she tried to escape. But in her hurry she slipped and fell down to the deepest depth of the mountains. Left alone, she realised how vain she was in trying to be different. Hearing her, the boy smiled and said, "You are no longer alone, my friend."

18 Silver Fir Cones

Once there lived a miner with his wife and seven children. One day, he fell sick and could not go out to work. Since there was no food, his wife went up the mountains to get some fir cones so that she could sell them in the town and get some meat. When she started collecting fir cones in the forest, a dwarf with a white beard appeared before her. "What's the matter? Why are you stealing my fir cones," the dwarf frowned. The woman burst into tears and told her sad story. The dwarf then gave her some leaves to cure her husband and allowed her to collect as many fir cones as she wanted. The woman went home happily with her basket full of fir cones. She opened the basket and lo! The fir cones had turned to silver. She realised that the dwarf was Gubich, the king of dwarfs and thanked him in her prayers.

19 Hodja's Donkey

One day, Mullah Nasruddin Hodja took his donkey to the market and sold it for thirty dinars. The man who had bought it immediately put it up for auction. He started his bidding and shouted to the passersby about the donkey's qualities, calling it a rare specimen. Hearing him, a man came forward and agreed to give forty dinars for it, while another volunteered to buy it for fifty dinars. Mullah was standing nearby and was amazed at the interest shown to his donkey. "Oh! What a fool I am," thought Nasruddin. "It was an extraordinary animal and I never knew it. I thought this was…" Suddenly, he realised that the man was about to close the bidding. "Seventy five dinars, one" shouted the man. "Seventy five dinars two, seventy five dinars…" "Eighty dinars," screamed Nasruddin and bought his donkey back.

20 Out on a Limb

Once, Mullah Nasruddin climbed up a tree and started sawing that very branch on which he was sitting. Clever Peter saw him and asked him not to do so as he would fall along with the branch. Mullah ignored his advice and continued sawing the branch until it was cut and he fell down. Then he thought that Clever Peter should be a fortune teller since he predicted his fall from the tree. So Nasruddin went up to him and asked about the longevity of his life. Clever Peter felt amused and advised Nasruddin to count the number of times his donkeys burped after dinner and that he would live as many years. That night, Nasruddin counted his donkey burping seven times. After seven years, thinking he would die, he dug a grave for himself and lay there waiting for death. Just then, a herd of camels was passing by. The first camel accidentally fell into the grave and tumbled all over Nasruddin. Next two followed too. At the end, Nasruddin returned home all bruised.

21 Goodness Begets Reward

Archana and Aradhana were the two beautiful daughters of a rich merchant. The news of their beauty spread and reached the young king's ears, who was on the lookout for a bride. So he decided to marry one of the merchant's daughters. But he was confused as to which one would be an ideal wife as both were equally beautiful. "Let me disguise myself as a poor man and test how good human beings the two beautiful ladies are," thought the king.

So the king disguised himself as a poor farmer and met the girls while they were taking their evening walk in their garden. "Dear ladies, I am hungry for days. Please me give something to eat," pleaded the disguised king. Archana at once shouted out, "Go away, you old haggard!" But Aradhana took out two gold coins and handed it to the poor man saying, "Buy yourself some food" and walked away. This was enough for the king to decide who would be his future bride. He married Aradhana and took her to his palace.

22 How Abu Nawasi Sold His House

Abu Nawasi built a two-storied house for himself. He lived in the lower storey and sold the upper one to a merchant. After a few years, Abu Nawasi decided to shift to some other place. Everything was ready, there was one problem. It seemed that no one was interested to buy the lower storey. The merchant too flatly refused him. But in fact, he intended to grab the lower storey and confided in his wife about his intentions. Abu overheard him and decided to trick this greedy man into buying the lower storey. He went out and brought twelve workers with him. He told the merchant, "Since I cannot sell my house, I have hired these people to help me destroy it. Do whatever you can to save your upper storey." Hearing this, the merchant readily agreed to buy the storey at the price that Abu Nawasi was demanding.

23 Witness

Once a man borrowed a sum of money from a rich farmer and did not return it. Instead, he trapped the farmer in a deserted place and threatened to kill him. The farmer pleaded the borrower to leave him and assured him that the borrower wouldn't have to repay. He readily made a receipt stating he had been repaid keeping the banyan tree as the witness. But next day, the king sent for him. "Why haven't you repaid the money to this man," inquired the king. The borrower stated that he had returned the farmer's money in the presence of the banyan tree and showed the king the receipt. The king understood that the man was a liar and shouted out in anger, "You liar! You'll have to pay him back since there is no signature of the banyan tree and no receipt is complete without the witness' signature. Moreover, no one keeps a banyan tree as a witness. And you'll be punished for forcing this man to sign this receipt."

24 The Crane's Reward

One day, a lion was feasting on a zebra with his family when a small bone got caught in his throat. The lioness ran from pillar to post to get hold of somebody who could take the bone out. But no one dared to put its head into the lion's mouth. At last, the lion met a crane. "O good crane! Please help me. You have a long thin neck. Only you can help me out," roard he. "I shall reward you," he continued, "and don't worry I won't harm you. After all, who would then help me out of this pain," he assured. The greedy crane could not resist the promise of a reward. He ordered the lion to open his mouth wide. Then he stuck its bill into the lion's throat and in no time, he brought the bone out of the lion's throat. The crane then demanded his reward. "Don't you think you have got your reward? You ordered a lion, you put your head into his mouth and still you're living," howled the lion. The crane knew better not to argue with him and flew away.

25 The Big Leap

One day, two frogs were so engrossed in chatting while hopping on their way that they didn't notice a deep ditch gaping wide a few paces ahead of them. "H-h-e-e-e-l-p!" they screamed loud while falling into the pit. Hearing their cries, all the frogs of the locality gathered around the pit. "Oh! They would die if we don't bring them out," said one. So they first gathered some sticks, tied them with ropes and held it out to them so that they could climb up. But even after tying the sticks together it was not long enough to reach them. Then they found a long rope, dropped one of its end to them holding the other end tight. But the two frogs slipped while climbing it up. The other frogs then gave it up. "We are very sorry. We can't take you out," they said apologetically. On hearing this, one frog lost heart and died in fear. The other frog panicked too. But he couldn't think of dying there like that. So with a terrible urge to live, he gathered all his energy and gave one great jump and that landed him out of the pit.

26 Why the Rabbit Has a Short Tail

Long ago, when the rabbit used to have a long tail, he often disturbed the fox lashing his long tail. One day, Fox returned home with a basket full of fish. Seeing this, Rabbit asked, "Brother Fox, how did you manage to catch so many fishes?" The Fox thought this to be the right time to do something about Rabbit's long tail and said, "Oh nothing. All you need to do is sit with your tail immersed in the water overnight and catch as many fishes as you want". The Rabbit believed him and went fishing the next night. He did exactly what Fox had told him, quite unaware that Fox wanted to get his tail frozen. All night long, Rabbit sat shivering on a log with his tail in the water. In the morning when he tried pulling out his tail, it was frozen. "Help!" cried out Rabbit and the Owl pulled him out by his ears. But lo! His ears grew long and the tail came off.

27 The Red-Handed Thieves

Once, many mysterious thefts plagued the state of Vijaynagar. Despite the strict security vigil, the number of thefts continued to increase till it took an alarming turn. Tenalirama decided to nab the thieves. He then contacted the richest jeweler of the state and asked him to organise an exhibition of his entire collection. The exhibition was a grand success and many people attended it. After the exhibition was over, Tenalirama put all the jewels in a bag and kept it locked in an iron safe. But, that night too the theft was committed. The king along with Tenalirama came to the site. Tenali ordered the guards to search everywhere in the locality and catch anyone with red grease paint on his hands and clothes. Soon, the thieves were identified and caught as Tenalirama had painted the safe red the night before and it was not yet dry.

28 Greater Than God

Two poets once praised Emperor Akbar highly in their poems comparing him with God and were handsomely rewarded. The courtesans were shocked to hear this but none dared to contradict. Akbar looked amused and everyone wondered if he had actually believed the poet and thought himself to be greater than God. There was silence in the courtroom and then everyone nodded their head in agreement. This made Akbar frown and then he turned to Birbal and asked, "Birbal, do you think I'm actually greater than God?" Birbal thought for a while and said very deftly, "My Lord, I think God cannot do certain things which you can. He cannot banish anyone the way you do from your kingdom for he owns the whole universe." Akbar understood Birbal's message and laughed out saying, "Indeed Birbal, you are great. None can surpass your wittiness."

29 The Loyal Gardener

One day, Emperor Akbar stumbled over a rock in his garden. He was not in a good mood that day and his head blew off in anger. He ordered the gardener to be executed. The next day, before the execution, the gardener requested to have an interview with the emperor as his last wish. The wish was granted. But as the gardener neared the throne, he spat at the emperor's feet. The emperor was stunned at his impudence. The gardener did it on Birbal's advice and now Birbal came forward and explained, "Your Majesty! He is a loyal gardener. Fearing that people might say that you've hanged him for no reason, he gave you a genuine reason for hanging him." The emperor realised his mistake and set the man free.

30 A Family of Tyrants

A shopkeeper of Isfahan went to the governor with a request to exempt him from the tax since he was not doing well. The governor refused to do so and ordered him to go to cities like Shiraz or Kashan if he could not pay his tax. The shopkeeper said that he would face the same problems in Shiraz or Kashan since both were ruled by the governor's nephew and cousin respectively. "Even, I can't go to the king complaining about this law since your brother who is his prime minister has a tremendous influence on him," complained the shopkeeper. "Then you go to the other world," howled the governor. "Yes I can," said the shopkeeper, "but didn't your father die last year?" The governor burst into laughter and exempted his tax.

31 A Matter of Crows

Emperor Akbar was highly amused with Birbal's ready wit. He would often praise him in the court saying, "Birbal, your intelligence and wit is indeed incomparable." His courtiers felt that Akbar was biased and asked him to test Birbal's intelligence. One morning, while Emperor Akbar was taking a stroll in his garden, a flock of crows were sitting atop a tree and cawing loudly. Akbar looked up and suddenly an idea struck him. He summoned all his courtiers and said, "Tell me the exact number of crows that are there in Agra. I need the information now. Whosoever can say so, will not only be handsomely rewarded, but will also be acknowledged the cleverest man in the kingdom." All his courtiers were mum. Only Birbal answered with a smile, "Your Majesty! There are ten thousand, six hundred and sixty- six crows in all of Agra. You can't get away by stating a figure. We shall have a proper count to see whether you are correct," said Akbar grinning. "That's fine, Your Majesty!" replied Birbal, "but I can't assure you that all crows will remain in Agra till that. Some may go out to visit friends and some more may come to visit their friends here. So the number may vary." The emperor laughed and praised Birbal for his ready wit.

OTHER TITLES IN THIS SERIES

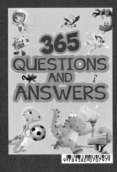

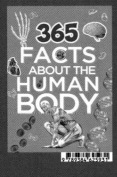

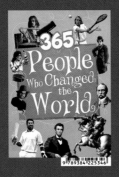

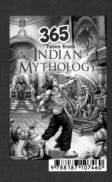
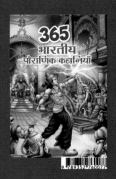

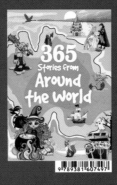